Elementary
Survey Sampling

William Mendenhall
Lyman Ott
Richard L. Scheaffer

University of Florida

Wadsworth Publishing Company, Inc.
Belmont, California

L. C. Cat. Card No.: 74–126361
Printed in the United States of America

1 2 3 4 5 6 7 8 9 10—75 74 73 72 71

Contents

1 Introduction

2 A Review of Some Basic Concepts

2.1 Introduction   *5*

2.2 Describing a Set of Measurements   *6*

2.3 Probability   *7*

2.4 Random Variables and Probability Distribution   *9*

2.5 Expectations   *10*

2.6 Covariance and Correlation   *11*

2.7 The Central Limit Theorem and the Normal Distribution   *13*

2.8 Point Estimation and Interval Estimation   *14*

2.9 Summary   *15*

3 Elements of the Sampling Problem

3.1 Introduction   *19*

3.2 Technical Terms   *20*

3.3   How to Select the Sample: The Design
       of the Sample Survey   *22*

3.4   Methods of Data Collection   *24*

3.5   Designing a Questionnaire   *26*

3.6   Summary   *27*

4   Simple Random Sampling

4.1   Introduction   *31*

4.2   How to Draw a Simple Random
       Sample   *32*

4.3   Estimation of a Population Mean and
       Total   *33*

4.4   Selecting the Sample Size for Estimating
       Population Means and Totals   *39*

4.5   Estimation of a Population
       Proportion   *43*

4.6   Summary   *48*

5   Stratified Random Sampling

5.1   Introduction   *53*

5.2   How to Draw a Stratified Random
       Sample   *54*

5.3   Estimation of a Population Mean and
       Total   *56*

5.4   Selecting the Sample Size for Estimating
       Population Means and Totals   *60*

5.5   Allocation of the Sample   *64*

5.6   Estimation of a Population
       Proportion   *73*

5.7   Selecting the Sample Size and Allocating
       the Sample to Estimate Proportions   *76*

5.8   Additional Comments on Stratified
       Sampling   *82*

5.9   Summary   *87*

6   Ratio Estimation

6.1   Introduction   *93*

6.2   Surveys That Require the Use of Ratio
       Estimators   *94*

6.3   Ratio Estimation Using Simple Random
Sampling   *95*

6.4   Selecting the Sample Size   *104*

6.5   When to Use Ratio Estimation   *113*

6.6   Summary   *114*

7   Cluster Sampling

7.1   Introduction   *121*

7.2   How to Draw a Cluster Sample   *122*

7.3   Estimation of a Population Mean and
Total   *123*

7.4   Selecting the Sample Size for Estimating
Population Means and Totals   *132*

7.5   Estimation of a Population
Proportion   *137*

7.6   Selecting the Sample Size for Estimating
Proportions   *139*

7.7   Summary   *141*

8   Systematic Sampling

8.1   Introduction   *147*

8.2   How to Draw a Systematic Sample   *149*

8.3   Estimation of a Population Mean and
Total   *150*

8.4   Estimation of a Population
Proportion   *156*

8.5   Selecting the Sample Size   *158*

8.6   Repeated Systematic Sampling   *161*

8.7   Summary   *165*

9   Two-Stage Cluster Sampling

9.1   Introduction   *171*

9.2   How to Draw a Two-Stage Cluster
Sample   *172*

9.3   Unbiased Estimation of a Population
Mean and Total   *173*

9.4   Ratio Estimation of a Population
Mean   *178*

9.5   Estimation of a Population Proportion   *181*

9.6   Summary   *183*

10   Sampling from Wildlife Populations

10.1   Introduction   *187*

10.2   Estimation of a Population Size Using Direct Sampling   *188*

10.3   Estimation of a Population Size Using Inverse Sampling   *190*

10.4   Choosing Sample Sizes for Direct and Inverse Sampling   *192*

10.5   Summary   *196*

11   Supplemental Topics

11.1   Introduction   *201*

11.2   Interpenetrating Subsamples   *202*

11.3   Estimation of Means and Totals over Subpopulations   *204*

11.4   Random Response Model   *210*

11.5   Summary   *213*

12   Summary   *217*

Appendix

Normal Curve Areas   *223*

Squares and Square Roots   *224*

Random Digits   *238*

Answers   *241*

Index   *245*

Preface

Elementary Survey Sampling is an introductory text on the design and analysis of sample surveys intended for students of business, the social sciences, or natural-resource management. The only prerequisite is an elementary course in statistics. The numerous examples, with solutions, also make it suitable for use as a supplemental text for higher level courses.

Since it is written to appeal to students of limited mathematical background, the text emphasizes the practical aspects of survey problems. Each major chapter introduces a sample survey design or a possible estimation procedure by describing a pertinent practical problem and then explaining the suitability of the methodology proposed. This introduction is followed by the appropriate estimation procedures and a compact presentation of the formulae; then a practical example is worked out. The text is not entirely cookbook in nature. Explanations that appeal to the students' intuition are supplied to justify many of the formulae and to support the choice of particular sample survey designs. Examples and exercises have been selected from many fields of application. Answers, which are given for all exercises, may be subject to small rounding errors because of the complexity of some of the formulae.

The text includes a review of elementary concepts (Chapters 1 and 2) and a description of terms pertinent to survey sampling, along with a discussion of the design of questionnaires and methods of data collection (Chapter 3). Chapters

4, 5, 7, and 8 present the four most common sample survey designs—namely, simple random sampling, stratified random sampling, cluster sampling, and systematic sampling, respectively. Chapter 6 discusses ratio estimation. The remaining chapters deal with two-stage cluster sampling, sampling of animal populations, and other specialized problems that occur in survey sampling.

We wish to express our sincere appreciation to the many people who have helped in the preparation of this text. Particular thanks are due to the reviewers for their helpful comments during the preparation of this manuscript. Thanks are also due to Professor A. Hald for his kind permission to use the table of normal curve areas reprinted in the appendix. We are also deeply indebted to the typists who have given much of their time in preparing this text: Judith Donnelley, Mary Jackson, Catherine Kennedy, and Shirley Morley. Finally, we thank our families for assistance and encouragement throughout the duration of this project.

William Mendenhall
Lyman Ott
Richard L. Scheaffer

1 Introduction

Introductory courses stress the fact that modern statistics is a theory of information with inference as its objective. The target of our curiosity is a set of measurements, a *population*, that exists in fact or could be generated by repeated experimentation. The medium of inference is the *sample*, which is a subset of measurements selected from the population. We wish to make an inference about the population based on the characteristics of the sample—or, equivalently, the information contained in the sample.

For example, suppose that a chain of department stores maintains customer charge accounts. The amount of money owed the company will vary from day to day as new charges are made and some accounts are paid. Indeed, the set of amounts due the company on a given day represents a population of measurements of considerable interest to the management. The population characteristic of interest is the total of all measurements in the population or, equivalently, the daily total credit load.

Keeping track of the daily total credit associated with charge accounts might seem to be a simple task for an electronic computer. However, the data must be updated daily, and this takes time. A simpler method for determining the total credit load associated with the charge accounts would be to randomly sample the population of accounts on a given day, estimate the average amount owed per account, and multiply by the number of accounts. In other words, we would employ a statistical estimator to make an inference about the population total. Elementary statistics tells us that this estimate can be made as accurate

1

as we wish simply by increasing the sample size. The resulting estimate either would be accompanied by a bound on the error of estimation (Mendenhall, 1971, Chapter 8) or would be expressed as a confidence interval. Thus, information in the sample is used to make an inference about the population.

Since the objective of modern statistics is inference, the reader may question what particular aspect of statistics will be covered in a course on sample survey design. The answer to this is twofold. First, we will focus on the economics of purchasing a specific quantity of information. More specifically, how can we design sampling procedures that reduce the cost of a fixed quantity of information? Although introductory courses in statistics acknowledge the importance of this subject, they place major emphasis on basic concepts and on how to make inferences in specific situations *after* the data have been collected. The second distinguishing feature of our topic is that it is aimed at the particular types of sampling situations and inferential problems most frequently encountered in business, the social sciences, and natural-resource management (timber, wildlife, and recreation), rather than in the physical sciences.

Even the terminology of the social scientist differs from that of the physical scientist. Social scientists conduct *surveys* to collect a sample, while physical scientists perform *experiments*. Thus, we acknowledge that differences exist from one field of science to another in the nature of the populations and the manner in which a sample can be drawn. For example, populations of voters, financial accounts, or animals of a particular species may contain only a small number of elements. In contrast, the conceptual population of responses generated by measuring the yield of a chemical process is very large indeed. (You may recall that the properties of estimators and test statistics covered in most introductory courses assume that the population of interest is large relative to the sample.) Limitations placed on the sampling procedure also vary from one area of science to another. Sampling in the biological and physical sciences can frequently be performed under controlled experimental conditions. Such control is frequently impossible in the social sciences, business, and natural-resource management. For example, a medical researcher might compare the growth of rats subjected to two different drugs. For this experiment the initial weights of the rats and the daily intake of food could be controlled to reduce unwanted variation in the experiment. In contrast, very few variables can be controlled in comparing the effect of two different television advertisements on sales for a given product; no control is possible when studying the effect of environmental conditions on the number of seals in the North Pacific Ocean.

In summary, this text is concerned with the peculiarities of sampling and inference commonly encountered in business, the social sciences, and natural-resource management. Specifically, we will consider methods for actually selecting the sample from an existing population and ways of circumventing various difficulties that arise. Methods for designing surveys that capitalize on characteristics of the population will be presented along with associated estimators to reduce the cost for acquiring an estimate of specified accuracy.

Chapter 2 reviews some of the basic concepts encountered in introductory statistics, including the fundamental role that probability plays in making inferences. Chapter 3 presents some of the basic terminology of sampling, as well as a discussion of problems arising in sample survey design. Simple random sampling, familiar to the beginning student, is carefully presented in Chapter 4; it includes physical procedures for actually selecting the sample. Following chapters cover economical methods for selecting a sample and associated methods for estimating population parameters.

In reading this text, keep in mind that the ultimate objective of each chapter is *inference*. Identify the sampling procedure associated with each chapter, the population parameters of interest, their estimators and associated bounds on the errors of estimation. Develop an intuitive understanding and appreciation for the benefits to be derived from specialized sampling procedures. Focus on the broad concepts and do not become hypnotized by the formulas for estimators and variances that sometimes are unavoidably complicated. In short, one should focus on the forest rather than the trees. Work some exercises and the details will fall into place.

References

"Careers in Statistics," *American Statistical Association* and the *Institute of Mathematical Statistics*, 1962.

Mendenhall, William, *Introduction to Probability and Statistics*, 3d ed., Belmont, Calif.: Wadsworth Publishing Company, Inc., 1971.

2 A Review of Basic Concepts

2.1 Introduction

Knowledge of the basic concepts of statistics is a prerequisite for a study of sample survey design. The reader must know that the ultimate objective of statistics is to make inferences about a population based on information contained in a sample. The target of our inference, the population, is a set of measurements, finite or infinite, existing or conceptual. Hence, the first step in statistics is to find a way to phrase an inference about a population or, equivalently, to describe a set of measurements. Thus, frequency distributions and numerical descriptive measures are the first topic of our review.

The second step is to consider how inferences can be made about the population based on information contained in a sample. To do this let us first consider the role probability plays in making inferences. We note that the probabilist assumes a population to be known and makes inferences concerning the nature of a sample. Thus, he assumes a die to be balanced and infers the likelihood of a 6 on a single toss. The statistician uses probability in reverse. Knowing the probability of the sample, he infers the nature of the population from which the sample was drawn. While not essential, a brief review of the basic concepts of probability will be helpful in our study.

The method of inference primarily employed in business and the social sciences is estimation. We may wish to estimate the total assets of a corporation, the fraction of voters favoring candidate Jones, or the number of campers

5

using a state park during a given period of time. Hence, we must understand the basic concepts underlying the selection of an estimator of a population parameter, the method for evaluating its goodness, and the concepts involved in interval estimation. Because the bias and variance of estimators determine their goodness, we need to review the basic ideas concerned with the expectation of a random variable and the notions of variance and covariance.

The subsequent sections follow the outline given above. We begin with a review of the primary problem, namely, how to describe a set of measurements. We then rapidly review the probabilistic model for the repetition of an experiment. We explain how the model can be used to infer the characteristics of a population and discuss random variables, probability distributions, and expectations. The Central Limit Theorem, which justifies the normality of the distributions of many estimators, is fundamental to any discussion of inference. Finally, we present the basic concepts associated with point and interval estimation.

2.2   Describing a Set of Measurements

You recall that any set of measurements (population, sample, or any other set) can be described by constructing a frequency histogram for the data (Mendenhall, 1971, Chapter 3). A second method for describing a set of measurements uses numerical descriptive measures.

The mean, median, and mode are numerical descriptive measures that locate the center of a frequency distribution. The range, variance, and standard deviation measure variation, or spread, in a set of measurements. We are primarily interested in the mean as a measure of central tendency of a distribution of measurements and in the variance and standard deviation as measures of variation.

To review, the mean of a sample of n measurements, $y_1, y_2, \ldots, y_n$, is

$$\bar{y} = \frac{\sum_{i=1}^{n} y_i}{n}.$$

The symbol for the corresponding population mean is μ.

The variance of a set of n sample measurements is defined to be the average of the square of the deviations of the measurements about their mean. The population variance is denoted by the symbol σ^2.

The standard deviation, which is the square root of the variance, acquires significance as a measure of variation when interpreted using Tchebysheff's Theorem and the Empirical Rule.

Tchebysheff's Theorem states that *at least* $(1 - 1/k^2)$ of a set of measurements will lie within k standard deviations of their mean. For example, letting $k = 2$, one would expect at least 3/4 of a set of measurements to lie within two standard deviations of their mean. Tchebysheff's Theorem gives a lower bound on the fraction contained in an interval. In most instances the fraction contained in the interval will be substantially in excess of that indicated by Tchebysheff's Theorem. Indeed, the fractions will most frequently be closely approximated by those given in the Empirical Rule.

The Empirical Rule applies exactly to data that are normally distributed but gives a reasonably good approximation to any set of measurements that possesses a mound-shaped frequency distribution. The Empirical Rule states that approximately

68% of the measurements will lie in the interval $\mu \pm \sigma$,
95% of the measurements will lie in the interval $\mu \pm 2\sigma$,
99.7% of the measurements will lie in the interval $\mu \pm 3\sigma$.

The measurements of primary interest to a statistician are the set of estimates generated by an estimator in repeated sampling. Tchebysheff's Theorem and the Empirical Rule imply that most (at least 75% and likely 95%) of the estimates generated in repeated sampling will lie within *two standard deviations* of the mean of the estimator. The standard deviation to which we refer is a measure of variation of the conceptual distribution of estimates generated by repeated sampling.

The standard deviations of most estimators depend on the population variance, σ^2. The quantity

$$s^2 = \frac{\sum_{i=1}^{n} (y_i - \bar{y})^2}{n - 1}$$

is used throughout this text as an estimator of σ^2. We refer to this as the "*sample variance*."

2.3 Probability

While not absolutely prerequisite to a methodologically oriented study of sample survey design, it is useful to review the role that probability plays in making inferences and to briefly summarize the elements of the theory of probability. A more detailed discussion of this topic can be found in Mendenhall, 1971, Chapter 4.

To illustrate the way probability is used in making inferences, let us hypothesize that a certain political candidate, Jones, will win an election (that is, more than 50% of the voting population will favor Jones). A random sample of ten voters is drawn from the voting population, and each states that he will not vote for Jones. What do we infer about the population of "yes's" and "no's" corresponding to the preferences of eligible voters? Most would infer that fewer than 50% favor Jones, and this inference demonstrates the logic involved in our discussion. Assuming more than 50% of the population will vote for Jones we do not conclude that it is *impossible* to draw ten voters out of ten who do not favor him. *Rather, we intuitively feel that the observed sample is highly improbable, assuming Jones a winner*. The theory of probability tells us this event is very improbable, and, consequently we conclude that the fraction of voters favoring Jones is actually less than 50%. Thus, we have made an inference about the population of voters. The probability of observing the sample of ten "no's," assuming Jones a "winner," was instrumental in making the inference.

The theory of probability begins with the notion of an *experiment*, which is the process of making an observation. The exact procedure in which the observation is made must be clearly specified.

Experiments result in outcomes which vary in a random manner and are called *events*. A very special type of event, a *simple event*, is one which cannot be separated or decomposed into two or more other events. A specification of the experiment and a complete listing of all simple events provide a complete description of a single repetition of the experiment. Simple events are mutually exclusive because one and only one can be observed for a single repetition of the experiment (that is, occurrence of one simple event excludes the occurrence of another).

It is convenient to define a one-to-one correspondence between simple events and points, so that a set of simple events can be viewed as a collection of sample points.

Events can be decomposed into one or more simple events, or equivalently, sample points. Thus, tossing a die can yield the event, "observe an even number." This event, in turn, can be decomposed into the three sample points associated with the observation of a 2, 4, and a 6. Consequently, *an event is defined to be a collection of sample points* corresponding to the simple events into which it can be decomposed. One additional important characteristic of events and sample points is that an event will occur if any sample point (simple event) in the event occurs.

To complete the probabilistic model for the repetition of an experiment, we assign a probability to each sample point in such a way that the probabilities of the simple events, $E_1, E_2, \ldots, E_k$, satisfy the properties

$$0 \le P(E_i) \le 1$$

and

$$\sum_{i=1}^{k} P(E_i) = 1.$$

Thus, in a sense we have constructed a model for a conceptual population that could be generated by repetition of the experiment.

The objective of the theory of probability is to deduce the outcome of an experiment given knowledge of the population (that is, the probabilistic model). We do this by calculating a measure of belief in the occurrence of the event; we call this its probability. Recall that the probability of an event can be systematically acquired by summing the probabilities of all sample points in the event.

We can also calculate the probability of an event by using event compositions. To do this we need knowledge of conditional probability, mutually exclusive events, complementary events, and independence. Thus, the definitions of union and intersection along with the additive and multiplicative laws of probability provide a second way to calculate the probability of an event. We will not elaborate further on the theory of probability. The reader interested in a more comprehensive treatment of the subject can consult the reference at the end of the chapter.

2.4   Random Variables and Probability Distributions

In most sampling situations we are interested in experiments which lead to numerical outcomes. For example, in an election survey we might want to predict the proportion of the popular vote that will go to candidate Jones. The numerical event of interest would be the fraction of the voters from the sample who prefer Jones.

Let y denote the variable of interest in a particular experiment. The numerical events of interest will be all possible values that y may assume. Recall that an event was defined to be a collection of sample points. Thus, we define a random variable to be a numerical-valued function defined over a sample space, because it will assume a value associated with each point in the sample space.

It is important to draw a distinction between two types of random variables. A *discrete* random variable is one which can assume a finite or countable infinity of values. In most instances discrete random variables represent count data such as the number of consumers who prefer product X. A random variable that may assume the infinitely large number of values on a line interval is called a *continuous* random variable. Heights and weights may be considered continuous random variables depending on the accuracy of the measuring equipment.

The probability distribution for a discrete random variable y refers to a formula, graph, or table which provides the probability $p(y)$ assigned to each value of y. These probabilities satisfy the following conditions:

$$0 \le p(y) \le 1$$

and

$$\sum_{\text{all } y} p(y) = 1.$$

More detailed discussions of random variables and their probability distributions are referenced at the end of this chapter.

2.5 Expectations

The probability distribution for a random variable is a theoretical model for a population frequency distribution of data that could be generated by a large number of repetitions of the experiment. Consequently, we are interested in acquiring numerical descriptive measures for this distribution. These are called parameters of the distribution. Thus, if y is a discrete random variable with probability distribution $p(y)$, the expected value of y, denoted by the symbol $E(y)$, is defined as

$$E(y) = \sum_{\text{all } y} y p(y).$$

If $p(y)$ is a perfect model of the population frequency distribution, then $E(y)$ is equal to the population mean, μ.

In a similar way we can define the expected value of functions of the random variable y. Let $g(y)$ be some numerical function of the random variable y; then the average or expected value of $g(y)$ is given by

$$E[g(y)] = \sum_{\text{all } y} g(y) p(y).$$

One of the most important functions of a random variable y used in describing its probability distribution is its variance, which measures the dispersion of y about its mean, μ. Symbolically, the variance of y is given by

$$E(y - \mu)^2 = \sum_{\text{all } y} (y - \mu)^2 p(y),$$

which is often denoted by the symbol σ^2.

The expected values and variances of important estimators (random variables) discussed in following chapters will not be derived, but knowledge of the concept of an expectation and how it is acquired will help you understand this material.

2.6   Covariance and Correlation

Often an experiment yields more than one random variable of interest. For example, the psychologist measures more than one characteristic per individual in a study of human behavior. Typical variables might be a measure of intelligence, y_1, a personality measure, y_2, and other variables representing test scores or measures of physical characteristics. Often we are interested in the simple dependence of pairs of variables, such as the relationship between personality and intelligence, or between college achievement and college board scores. Particularly, we ask whether data representing paired observations of y_1 and y_2 on a number of people imply a dependence between the two variables. If so, how strong is the dependence?

Intuitively, we think of dependence of two random variables, y_1 and y_2, as implying that one, say y_1, either increases or decreases as y_2 changes. We will confine our attention to two measures of dependence, the *covariance* and the *simple coefficient of linear correlation*, and will utilize Figures 2.1 (a) and (b) to justify choosing them as measures of dependence. These figures represent plotted points for two (random) samples of $n = 10$ experimental units drawn from a population. Measurements of y_1 and y_2 were made on each experimental unit. If all of the points lie on a straight line, as indicated in Figure 2.1 (a), y_1 and y_2 are obviously dependent. In contrast, Figure 2.1 (b) indicates little or no dependence between y_1 and y_2.

Suppose we actually know μ_1 and μ_2, the means of y_1 and y_2, respectively, and locate this point on the graphs, Figure 2.1. Now locate a plotted point on Figure 2.1 (a) and measure the deviations, $(y_1 - \mu_1)$ and $(y_2 - \mu_2)$. Note that both deviations assume the same algebraic sign for a particular point; hence, their product, $(y_1 - \mu_1)(y_2 - \mu_2)$, is positive. This will be true for all plotted

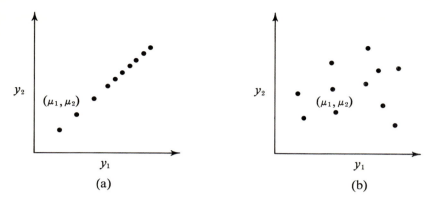

y_2 (μ_1, μ_2)

y_1

(a)

y_2 (μ_1, μ_2)

y_1

(b)

Figure 2.1

points on Figure 2.1 (a). Points to the right of (μ_1, μ_2) will yield pairs of positive deviations, points to the left will produce pairs of negative deviations, and the average of the product of the deviations, $(y_1 - \mu_1)(y_2 - \mu_2)$, will be "large" and positive. If the linear relation indicated in Figure 2.1 (a) had sloped downward to the right, all corresponding pairs of deviations would be of the opposite sign, and the average value of $(y_1 - \mu_1)(y_2 - \mu_2)$ would be a large negative number.

The situation described above will not occur for Figure 2.1 (b), where little or no dependence exists between y_1 and y_2. Corresponding deviations, $(y_1 - \mu_1)$ and $(y_2 - \mu_2)$, will assume the same algebraic sign for some points and opposite signs for others. Thus, the product

$$(y_1 - \mu_1)(y_2 - \mu_2)$$

will be positive for some points, negative for others, and will average to some value near zero.

Clearly, then, the expected (average) value of $(y_1 - \mu_1)(y_2 - \mu_2)$ provides a measure of the linear dependence of y_1 and y_2. This quantity, defined over the two corresponding populations associated with y_1 and y_2, is called the *covariance* of y_1 and y_2. We denote the covariance between y_1 and y_2 thus:

$$\text{Cov}(y_1, y_2) = E\{(y_1 - \mu_1)(y_2 - \mu_2)\}.$$

The larger the absolute value of the covariance of y_1 and y_2, the greater will be the linear dependence between y_1 and y_2. Positive values indicate that y_1 increases as y_2 increases; negative values indicate that y_1 decreases as y_2 increases. A zero value of the covariance indicates no linear dependence between y_1 and y_2.

Unfortunately, it is difficult to use the covariance as an absolute measure of dependence, because its value depends upon the scale of measurement. Consequently, it is difficult to determine whether a particular covariance is "large" at first glance. We can eliminate this difficulty by standardizing its value, using the simple coefficient of linear correlation. Thus, the population linear coefficient of correlation,

$$\rho = \frac{\text{Cov}(y_1, y_2)}{\sigma_1 \sigma_2},$$

(where σ_1 and σ_2 are the standard deviations of y_1 and y_2, respectively) is related to the covariance and can assume values in the interval $-1 \le \rho \le 1$. The sample coefficient of correlation is used as an estimator of ρ and is discussed in most introductory courses. Further information on this subject can be found in Mendenhall, 1971, Chapter 10.

2.7   The Central Limit Theorem and the Normal Distribution

Although the probability distributions for random variables possess a variety of shapes, many estimators possess a theoretical frequency distribution which is approximately bell-shaped or mound-shaped. One possible explanation is offered by the *Central Limit Theorem* which states that in repeated sampling, sums and means of samples of independent random observations drawn from a population tend to possess approximately a normal distribution.

The major significance of the Central Limit Theorem for sample survey methods is in statistical inference. In the succeeding chapters we find that many of the estimators of population parameters are either sums or averages of sample observations. Consequently, we can employ the Empirical Rule; we will expect 95% of all estimates to be within two standard deviations of their mean in repeated sampling.

Probability statements about a normal random variable require knowledge of the areas under the normal curve. Recall that the equation for the normal probability distribution depends on the values of μ and σ. Since separate tables are not available for each normal distribution, it is convenient to work with the areas under the standardized normal curve. These areas are presented in Table 1 of the Appendix. For our purposes we will utilize the few areas given in the Empirical Rule. Specifically, we need to know that approximately 95% of the area under a normal curve falls in the interval $\mu \pm 2\sigma$.

For a more thorough discussion of the normal distribution, including the calculation of areas under the standardized normal curve, consult Mendenhall, 1971, Chapter 7.

2.8   Point Estimation and Interval Estimation

The objective of a sample survey is to make inferences about the population of interest based on information obtained in the survey. Inferences of primary interest in sample survey methods are aimed at the estimation of certain population parameters.

You will recall that estimation procedures can be divided into two types, point estimation and interval estimation. A *point estimate* is a single number (or point) that is calculated from the sample measurements and that estimates the population parameter of interest. Two points that define an interval on a line form an *interval estimate* of a population parameter. The actual estimation is accomplished by an *estimator*, which is a rule that tells us how to calculate an estimate using the information contained in the sample. For example, the sample mean, $\bar{y}$, is an estimator of the population mean, μ. Thus,

$$\bar{y} = \frac{\sum\limits_{i=1}^{n} y_i}{n}$$

is a precise rule for computing an estimate using the sample observations $y_1, y_2, \ldots, y_n$.

As previously shown, we cannot evaluate the goodness of a point estimator based on only one estimate. Rather, we must consider the results which we would obtain if the estimation procedure were repeated many times. Certain desirable properties emerge. We would like the distribution of estimates to center about the parameter estimated. If $\hat{\theta}$ is a point estimator of θ, we would like the average or expected value of $\hat{\theta}$ to equal θ. Symbolically, we want

$$E(\hat{\theta}) = \theta.$$

An estimator that satisfies this property is said to be *unbiased*. We also would like the variance of the estimator, $\sigma_{\hat{\theta}}^2$, to be as small as possible. The goodness of a point estimator, $\hat{\theta}$, can then be evaluated in terms of its mean, $E(\hat{\theta})$, and variance, $\sigma_{\hat{\theta}}^2$.

We will define the error of estimation for an unbiased point estimator to be the distance that the estimate lies from the parameter. Symbolically,

$$\text{error of estimation} = |\hat{\theta} - \theta|.$$

How good will a single estimate be? We cannot state that $\hat{\theta}$ will definitely lie within a specified distance of θ, but we known from Tchebysheff's Theorem that *at least* 3/4 of the estimates generated in repeated sampling will lie within $2\sigma_{\hat{\theta}}$ of θ. Actually, the fraction of estimates in this interval will be nearer 95/100, because most distributions of estimates are relatively mound-shaped; hence, the Empirical Rule will apply. To rephrase in probability terms, the probability is approximately .95 that the error of estimation, $|\hat{\theta} - \theta|$, will be less than $2\sigma_{\hat{\theta}}$. Because most estimates will lie within $2\sigma_{\hat{\theta}}$ of θ, we say that $2\sigma_{\hat{\theta}}$ is a *bound on the error of estimation*. (One need not work with a probability of .95. The bound corresponding to any probability can be acquired using Tchebysheff's Theorem or areas under the normal curve, Table 1 of the Appendix.)

An interval estimator is evaluated in terms of the fraction of times in repeated sampling the interval estimate will enclose the parameter of interest.

Whether one uses a point estimate with a bound on the error of estimation or an interval estimate seems to be a matter of personal preference. We will use point estimators and give bounds on the error of estimation. In many situations these two different methods of estimation yield the same result.

2.9 Summary

Chapter 2 presents a capsule review of the basic concepts of statistics. Making an inference about a population requires a method for describing a set of measurements and, consequently, requires a discussion of frequency histograms and numerical descriptive measures. Two very useful numerical descriptive measures are the mean and standard deviation. Although the mean is an easily understood measure of central tendency, the standard deviation acquires meaning as a measure of variation only when interpreted using Tchebysheff's Theorem and the Empirical Rule.

Another important concept is the role that probability plays in making inferences about a population. The probabilist reasons from a known population to a sample. In contrast, the statistician uses probability as the vehicle to make inferences about a population based on information contained in a sample. The notion of a sample space for an experiment, which provides a mechanism for calculating the probability of an event, is a fundamental probabilistic concept.

Although a good background in probability is desirable, knowledge of the basic concepts of probability and the use of probability in inference-making provides a sufficient background for understanding this text.

Random variables and their probability distributions are presented to provide a background for describing the properties of estimators of population parameters. The notions of expectations, covariance, and correlation assist in evaluating the properties of estimators.

The estimation of population parameters is the primary method of inference-making used in sample survey methods. The concept of a point estimator with its corresponding measure of goodness (bound on the error of estimation) is presented and is used as the method of inference in all subsequent chapters.

Reference

Mendenhall, William, *Introduction to Probability and Statistics*, 3d ed., Belmont, Calif.: Wadsworth Publishing Company, Inc., 1971. Chapters 3, 4, 7, and 8.

Exercise

2.1   What is the objective of statistics?

2.2   How does a course on sample survey design differ from the standard introductory course on statistics?

2.3   Why is it essential to know how to describe a set of measurements?

2.4   How can you describe a set of measurements?

2.5   What is a parameter?

2.6   State Tchebysheff's Theorem.

2.7   State the Empirical Rule.

2.8   Given $n = 20$ sample measurements: 1, 2, 0, 2, 2, 4, 0, 3, 1, 2, 3, 2, 0, 1, 2, 2, 4, 2, 1, 3.
      (a) Calculate the sample mean, $\bar{y}$.
      (b) Calculate s^2.
      (c) What fraction of the measurements lie within one standard deviation of the mean? Two? Three? How do these fractions agree with those given by Tchebysheff's Theorem and the Empirical Rule? (This

example illustrates the effectiveness of the standard deviation as a measure of the variability of a set of measurements.)

2.9 Given $n = 10$ sample measurements: 5, 2, 4, 4, 3, 4, 1, 3, 5, 4.
(a) Calculate the sample mean.
(b) Calculate the sample variance.
(c) Find the fraction of measurements lying within one standard deviation of the mean. Compare these with the corresponding figures given by Tchebysheff's Theorem and the Empirical Rule.

2.10 What is the objective when calculating a sample mean and variance?

2.11 What do we mean when we say that two random variables are positively correlated? Negatively correlated?

2.12 What is an estimator?

2.13 How does one evaluate the goodness of an estimator?

2.14 Describe two desirable properties for an estimator.

2.15 What is an unbiased estimator?

2.16 What is the "error of estimation"?

2.17 What is a reasonable bound on the error of estimation?

2.18 Of what value are Tchebysheff's Theorem and the Empirical Rule in making statements about the error of estimation?

3 Elements of the Sampling Problem

3.1 Introduction

You will recall that the objective of statistics is to make inferences about a population based on information contained in a sample. This same objective motivates our discussion of the sampling problem. We will consider the particular problem of sampling from a finite collection of measurements (population). We will refer occasionally to populations composed of an infinite number of measurements. In most cases, the inference will be in the form of an estimate of a population parameter, such as a mean, total or proportion, with a bound on the error of estimation. For those more interested in methodology than theory, intuitive arguments will be given whenever possible to justify the use of estimators.

The first part of our discussion of the sampling problem introduces certain technical terms common to sample surveys. Next we discuss how to select a sample from the population of interest.

Each observation, or item, taken from the population contains a certain amount of information about the population parameter or parameters of interest. Since information costs money, the experimenter must determine how much information he should buy. Too little information prevents him from making good estimates, while too much information results in a waste of money. The quantity of information obtained in the sample depends upon the number of

19

items sampled and upon the amount of variation in the data. This latter factor can be controlled by the method of selecting the sample, called the *design of the sample survey*; it, along with the sample size, determines the quantity of information in the sample pertinent to a population parameter. Several sample survey designs are introduced in Section 3.3.

The design of the sample survey does not determine how the data are to be obtained once an item has been chosen for the sample. Thus we need to discuss methods of data collection. This is done in Section 3.4, with special emphasis on the advantages and limitations of each method.

3.2 Technical Terms

Technical terminology is kept to a minimum in this text; however, certain common terms must be defined. Let us introduce these terms by way of an example. In a certain community an opinion poll was conducted to determine public sentiment towards a bond issue in an upcoming election. The objective of the survey was to estimate the proportion of voters in the community who favored the bond issue.

Definition 3.1   An *element* is an object on which a measurement is taken.

In our example an element is a registered voter in the community. The measurement taken on an element is the voter's preference on the bond issue. Since measurements are usually considered to be numbers, the experimenter could obtain numerical data by recording a one for a voter in favor of the bond issue and a zero for a voter not in favor.

Definition 3.2   A *population* is a collection of measurements about which we wish to make an inference.

The population of interest should be clearly specified by the investigator. The bond issue population consists of the preferences of all registered voters in the community. Note that the word "population" refers to data and not people.

Definition 3.3   *Sampling units* are nonoverlapping collections of elements from the population.

A registered voter in the community is an element in the bond-issue example. However, it might be more convenient and less costly to sample households (groups of elements) rather than individual voters to obtain voter preferences. In that case, the units to be sampled (sampling units) would be households within the community. Note that each sampling unit consists of either none, one, or more than one element from the population, depending upon the number of eligible voters within a given household.

If each sampling unit contains one and only one element of the population, then a sampling unit and an element from the population are identical. This situation arises if we sample individual voters rather than households within the community.

Definition 3.4   A *frame* is a list of sampling units.

If we specify the individual voter as the sampling unit, a list of all registered voters could serve as a frame for a public opinion poll. Note that this frame would not include all the elements in the population, because it would be impossible to update the list daily. If we take the household as the sampling unit, then a telephone directory, a city directory, or a list of household heads obtained from census data could serve as a frame.

All of these frames would have some inadequacies. The lists would not be up-to-date. They would contain many names of unregistered household heads, and hence, a sample drawn from the lists would contain many units which are not in the population of interest. Also, some registered voters might not appear on any of these lists. Hopefully, however, the gap between the frame and the population is small enough to permit inferences to be made about the population based on a sample drawn from the frame.

Definition 3.5   A *sample* is a collection of sampling units drawn from a frame.

Data are obtained from the elements of the sample and used in describing the population of interest. Let the individual voter be our sampling unit and the list of registered voters be our frame. In the public opinion poll a number of voters (the sample) would be contacted to determine their preference for the upcoming bond issue. We then could use the information obtained from these voters to make an inference about the voter preference throughout the community.

3.3   How to Select the Sample : The Design of the Sample Survey

   The objective of sampling is to estimate population parameters, such as the mean or total, from information contained in a sample. As stated previously, the experimenter controls the quantity of information contained in the sample by the number of sampling units he includes in the sample and by the method he uses to select the sample data. How does one determine which procedure to use and the number of observations (sampling units) to include in the sample? The answer depends upon how much information the experimenter wants to buy. If θ is the parameter of interest and $\hat{\theta}$ is an estimator of θ, the experimenter should specify a bound on his error of estimation; that is, he should specify that θ and $\hat{\theta}$ differ in absolute value by less than some value B. Stated symbolically,

$$\text{error of estimation} = |\theta - \hat{\theta}| < B.$$

The experimenter also must state a probability, $(1 - \alpha)$, which specifies the fraction of times in repeated sampling he requires the error of estimation to be less than B. This can be stated

$$P[\text{error of estimation} < B] = 1 - \alpha.$$

We will usually select $B = 2\sigma_{\hat{\theta}}$, and hence, $(1 - \alpha)$ will be approximately .95 for mound-shaped distributions. Most estimators used in this book will exhibit mound-shaped distributions for reasonably large sample sizes, even when the parent population is skewed.

   After we obtain a specified bound with its associated probability, $(1 - \alpha)$, we can compare different designs (methods of selecting the sample) to determine which procedure yields the desired precision at minimum cost. The problem of selecting the sample size to achieve a certain bound on error is discussed in Mendenhall, 1971, Chapter 8.

   The basic design (*simple random sampling*) consists of selecting a group of n sampling units in such a way that each sample of size n has the same chance of being selected. Thus, we could obtain a random sample of n eligible voters in the bond issue poll by drawing names from the list of registered voters in such a way that each sample of size n has the same probability of selection. The details

of simple random sampling are discussed in Chapter 4. At this point, we merely state that a simple random sample would contain as much information on the community preference as any other sample survey design, provided all voters in the community have similar socioeconomic backgrounds.

Suppose, however, that the community consists of people in two distinct income brackets, high and low. Voters in the high bracket may have opinions on the bond issue which are quite different from those in the low bracket. Therefore, to obtain accurate information about the population, we want to sample voters from each bracket. We could divide the population elements into two groups, or strata, according to income and select a simple random sample from each group. The resulting sample is called a *stratified random sample*.

Note that stratification is accomplished by using knowledge of an auxiliary variable, namely personal income. By stratifying on high and low values of income, we increase the accuracy of our estimator. *Ratio estimation* is a second method for using the information contained in an auxiliary variable. Ratio estimators not only use measurements on the response of interest but also incorporate measurements on an auxiliary variable. Ratio estimation can be used with stratified random sampling; however, further discussion of this topic is beyond the scope of this text.

Although individual preferences are desired in the survey, it may be much more economical, especially in urban areas, to sample specific families, apartment buildings, or city blocks rather than individual voters. Individual preferences could then be obtained from each eligible voter within the unit sampled. This technique is called *cluster sampling*. Although we divide the population into groups for both cluster sampling and stratified random sampling, the techniques differ. In stratified random sampling we take a simple random sample within each group, while in cluster sampling we take a simple random sample of groups and then sample all items within the selected groups (clusters).

Sometimes the names of persons in the population of interest are available in a list, such as a registration list, or on file cards stored in a drawer. It is sometimes economical to draw the sample by selecting one name near the beginning of the list and then selecting every tenth or fifteenth name thereafter. If the sampling is conducted in this manner, we obtain a *systematic sample*. As you might expect, systematic sampling offers a convenient means of obtaining sample information; unfortunately, we do not necessarily obtain the most information for a specified amount of money.

We know that observations cost money. Note that the cost of an observation may vary from design to design, and even within a design, depending upon the method of data collection. The experimenter should choose the design which gives the desired bound on error with the smallest number of observations (assuming the same cost per observation). However, if the cost per observation varies from design to design, the experimenter should choose the design which gives the desired bound on the error of estimation at a minimum cost.

3.4 Methods of Data Collection

There are many different methods of collecting the sample data once the sampling design has been chosen. All sampling techniques and estimation procedures are based on the assumption that the sample data are drawn from the population of interest. Hence, drawing the sample is of prime importance. There are several problems to recognize. First, a nonresponse to a question put to an individual selected to be included in the sample can introduce a bias into the sample data. Those in the sample who do respond may not represent the population about which we wish to make inferences. For example, in a survey to determine employee acceptance of a monthly parking fee, it is quite likely only those people violently opposed to the fee would respond to a mailed questionnaire. If we were to consider the percentage of respondents favoring the fee, we would probably obtain a distorted estimate of the true percentages for the entire population.

The second problem is that respondents or measuring equipment frequently give false information. For example, if a person is asked in an interview whether he cheated on his income tax, for fear of discovery, he would probably respond negatively whether he had or had not. The same person, however, might give a truthful statement to the same question posed in a mailed questionnaire. As another example, forest areas measured on aerial photographs may always read either high or low because of an improperly calibrated planimeter. The important point is that we have both nonresponse and response errors which may creep into our sample data, and either can lead to results which are not representative of the population of interest.

The third problem concerns arbitrary changes in the sampled elements. Data must be obtained from the exact sampling units which were selected in accordance with a sampling design. An interviewer must not substitute a next-door neighbor for a person whose name was sampled. Theoretically, samples selected according to a design have known probabilities associated with them. These known probabilities allow us to calculate the expected values and variances of estimators, such as the sample mean, and thus to determine the goodness of these estimators. If haphazard substitutions are made in the sample, this probability structure is altered and the goodness of the estimator is uncertain.

Practically speaking, haphazard substitutions may bias the results. For example, suppose next-door neighbors are substituted for families not at home. This may lead to a sample which contains an unduly high proportion of families with children, because these families will more frequently be found at home. If the response of interest is dependent upon the number of children in the family, the resulting estimate will be biased.

Various methods of data collection are as follows:

1. *Personal Interviews:*   Data are frequently obtained by *personal interviews.* For example, we could use personal interviews with eligible voters to obtain a sample of the public sentiments towards a community bond issue. The procedure usually requires the interviewer to ask prepared questions and to record the respondent's answers. The primary advantage of these interviews is that people will usually respond when confronted in person. In addition, the interviewer can note specific reactions and eliminate misunderstandings about the questions being asked. The major limitations of the personal interview (aside from the cost involved) concern the interviewer. If he is not thoroughly trained, he may deviate from the required protocol, thus introducing a bias into the sample data. Any movement, facial expression, or statement by the interviewer could affect the response obtained. For example, a leading question such as, "Are you also in favor of the bond issue?" might tend to elicit a positive response. Finally, errors in recording the responses could also lead to erroneous results.

2. *Telephone interviews:*   Information can also be obtained from persons in the sample through *telephone interviews.* With the advent of wide area telephone service lines (WATS lines) an interviewer can place any number of calls to specified areas of the country for a fixed monthly rate. Surveys conducted through telephone interviews are frequently less expensive than personal interviews due to the elimination of travel expenses. The investigator can also monitor the interviews to be certain the specified interview procedure is being followed.

   We recommend that interviews conducted over the telephone be kept short and impersonal to maintain the interest of the respondent. The most important limitation on these interviews is that we restrict ourselves to persons who can be reached by telephone. This could lead to the selection of a sample that would not be from the population of interest. A classic example occurred in 1936 when a telephone survey was used to predict the results of the Presidential election between Alfred Landon and Franklin Roosevelt. The survey predicted that Landon would win. The prediction was in error because more Republicans than Democrats had telephones.

3. *Self-administered Questionnaires:*   Another useful method of data collection which we will discuss is the *self-administered questionnaire*, to be completed by the respondent. These questionnaires usually are mailed to the individuals included in the sample, although other distribution methods could be used. To encourage participation by the respondents, a questionnaire must be carefully constructed.

   The self-administered questionnaire does not require interviewers, and thus, its use results in a savings in the cost of the survey. This savings in cost is usually bought at the expense of a lower response rate. Nonresponse can be a problem in any form of data collection, but since we have the least contact with respondents in a mailed questionnaire, we frequently have the lowest rate of response. The low response rate can introduce a bias into the sample because the people who answer questionnaires may not be representative of the population of interest. To eliminate some of this bias, we frequently contact the respondents through follow-up letters, telephone interviews, or personal interviews.

4. *Direct Observation:*   The fourth method for collecting data is *direct observation.* For example, if we were interested in estimating the number of trucks that use a

particular road during the 4–6 p.m. rush hours, we could assign a person to count the number of trucks passing a specified point during this period. Possibly electronic counting equipment could also be used. The disadvantage of using an observer is the possibility of errors in observation.

3.5 Designing a Questionnaire

We previously mentioned that a questionnaire should be constructed to encourage participation by the respondents. The most frequently used questionnaires are the dichotomous, multiple-choice, and open-end types. The *dichotomous* type is the simplest form and requires that the respondent choose between one of two responses. For example, we could conduct a mail questionnaire on the bond issue by asking the following question:

> Are you in favor of the bond issue which is to be presented to the people in the upcoming election?
>
> ( ) YES   ( ) NO

Although the dichotomous questionnaire is easy to construct, it sometimes oversimplifies an issue and does not provide room for compromise. The *multiple-choice* type is more appropriate in certain situations. In our public opinion poll, we could ask the following question:

> How would you indicate your opinion on the bond issue to be presented to the people in the upcoming election?
> ( )   Strongly in favor
> ( )   In favor
> ( )   Undecided
> ( )   Not in favor
> ( )   Strongly not in favor

The type of questionnaire which allows a person the most freedom of response is the *open-end* questionnaire. For example, we could ask the following question:

> What is your opinion on the bond issue to be presented to the people in the upcoming election?
> Response_____

As you might expect, the disadvantage of such a questionnaire is the difficulty the experimenter has in classifying the results he obtains.

Several general comments can be made regardless of the type of questionnaire being used. Questions must be simple and phrased to imply the same meaning to all persons. The question, How many children are in your family? may lead to confusion over what is meant by "children" and "in your family." The following question would be less ambiguous:

> How many persons under the age of 21 live in your household and receive more than one half of their financial support from you?

The experimenter should avoid leading questions such as:

> Don't you think the courts are too lenient with criminals?

These questions suggest the answer which the interviewer wants to hear, and the respondent may agree with the interviewer simply because that is the easiest response.

Questions must offer an adequate choice of answers to avoid forcing an unrepresentative response. It is particularly important to allow for no response, even on simple questions. For example, some people do not know their own age, and many have no opinion on the government of the state.

The questionnaire should be kept as short as possible and should contain only questions pertinent to the objectives of the survey. People quickly become bored when answering a long list of questions, and this boredom leads to incorrect answers.

Questionnaires should be pretested on a small group of people before the actual survey is performed. This gives the experimenter an opportunity to observe errors and shortcomings.

3.6 Summary

The objective of a sample survey is to make inferences about the population of interest based on information contained in a sample. The population consists of the body of data about which we wish to make an inference and is composed of elements or bits of information. Nonoverlapping collections of elements from the population are called sampling units. The frame is a list of sampling units which we use to represent the population of interest. The sample is a collection of sampling units drawn from the frame. Using the sample data, we will estimate certain population parameters and place bounds on our error of estimation.

The quantity of information obtained from the sample can be controlled by the number of sampling units drawn and the sample design or method of data collection used. Some of the designs introduced are simple random sampling, stratified random sampling, cluster sampling, and systematic sampling. Each is discussed in detail in a later chapter. The best design for a given problem is the one which provides the necessary precision in terms of a bound on the error of estimation for a minimum cost.

After the design has been selected, there are various methods of collecting the sample data. Personal interviews, telephone interviews, direct observations, and questionnaires are discussed and assessed as means of collecting the sample data. Each method has its advantages and limitations.

In Section 3.5, we discussed the actual construction of questionnaires with reference to dichotomous, multiple-choice, and open-end type questionnaires. Again we emphasize the importance of obtaining information in the sample which is representative of the population of interest. This problem is of prime significance when we consider methods of data collection.

References

Cochran, W. G., *Sampling Techniques*, 2d ed., New York: John Wiley and Sons, Inc., 1963.

Deming, W. E., *Sample Design in Business Research*, New York: John Wiley and Sons, Inc., 1960.

Kish, L., *Survey Sampling*, New York: John Wiley and Sons, Inc., 1965.

Mendenhall, William, *Introduction to Probability and Statistics*, 3d ed., Belmont, Calif.: Wadsworth Publishing Company, Inc., 1971.

Exercises

3.1   An experimenter wants to estimate the average water consumption per family in a city. Discuss the relative merits of choosing individual families, dwelling units (single family houses, apartment buildings, etc.), and city blocks as sampling units. What would you use as a frame in each case?

3.2   A forester wants to estimate the total number of trees on a tree farm that possess diameters exceeding 12 inches. A map of the farm is available. Discuss the problem of choosing appropriate sampling units and an appropriate frame.

3.3 A safety expert is interested in estimating the proportion of automobile tires with unsafe tread. Should he use individual cars or collections of cars, such as those in parking lots, as sampling units? What could he use as a frame?

3.4 An industry is composed of many small plants located throughout the United States. An executive wants to survey the opinions of the employees on the vacation policy of the industry. What would you suggest he use as sampling units? What could he use as a frame?

3.5 A state department of agriculture desires to estimate the number of acres planted in corn within the state. Suggest possible sampling units and frames.

3.6 A political scientist wants to estimate the proportion of adult residents of a state who favor a unicameral legislature. Discuss possible sampling units and frames. Also, discuss the relative merits of personal interviews, telephone interviews, and mailed questionnaires as methods of data collection.

3.7 Discuss the relative merits of using personal interviews, telephone interviews, and mailed questionnaires as methods of data collection for each of the following situations:
   (a) A television executive wants to estimate the proportion of viewers in the country who are watching his network at a certain hour.
   (b) A newspaper editor wants to survey the attitudes of the public toward the type of news coverage offered by his paper.
   (c) A city commissioner is interested in determining how homeowners feel about a proposed zoning change.
   (d) A county health department wants to estimate the proportion of dogs that have had rabies shots within the last year.

4 Simple Random Sampling

4.1 Introduction

The objective of a sample survey is to make an inference about the population of interest based on information contained in a sample. Two factors affect the quantity of information contained in the sample, and, hence, affect the precision of our inference-making procedure. The first is the size of the sample selected from the population. The second is the amount of variation in the data; this can frequently be controlled by the method of selecting the sample. The procedure for selecting the sample is called the *sample survey design*. For a fixed sample size, *n*, we will consider various designs or *sampling* procedures for obtaining the *n* observations in the sample. Since observations cost money, a design which provides a precise estimator of the parameter of interest for a fixed sample size yields a savings in cost to the experimenter. The basic design or sampling technique, simple random sampling, is discussed in this chapter.

Definition 4.1   If a sample of size *n* is drawn from a population of size *N* in such a way that every possible sample of size *n* has the same chance of being selected, the sampling procedure is called ***simple random sampling***. The sample thus obtained is called a ***simple random sample***.

31

We will use simple random sampling to obtain estimators for population means, totals, and proportions.

Consider the following problem. A federal auditor is to examine the accounts for a city hospital. The hospital records obtained from a computer show a particular accounts receivable total, and the auditor must verify this total. If there are 28,000 open accounts in the hospital, the auditor cannot afford the time to examine every patient record to obtain a total accounts receivable figure. Hence, it becomes necessary to choose some sampling scheme for obtaining a representative sample of patient records. After examining the patient accounts in the sample, the auditor can then estimate the accounts receivable total for the entire hospital. If the computer figure lies within a specified distance of the auditor's estimate, the computer figure is accepted as valid. Otherwise more hospital records must be examined for possible discrepancies between the computer figure and the sample data.

Suppose that all $N = 28,000$ patient records are recorded on IBM cards and a sample of size $n = 100$ is to be drawn. The sample is called a simple random sample if every possible sample of $n = 100$ records has the same chance of being selected.

Two problems now face the experimenter: (1) how does he draw the simple random sample, and (2) how can he estimate the various population parameters of interest? These topics are discussed in the following sections.

4.2   How to Draw a Simple Random Sample

To draw a simple random sample from the population of interest is not as trivial as it may first appear. How can one draw a sample from a population in such a way that every possible sample of size n has the same chance of being selected? The experimenter might use his own judgment to "randomly" select the sample. This technique is frequently called haphazard sampling. A second technique, representative sampling, involves choosing a sample which the experimenter considers to be typical or representative of the population. Both haphazard and representative sampling are subject to the investigator's bias and, more importantly, they lead to estimators whose properties cannot be evaluated. Thus, neither of these techniques leads to a simple random sample.

Simple random samples can be selected using tables of random numbers. A table of random numbers is shown in Table 3 of the Appendix. To illustrate its use, let us consider the following example.

Example 4.1

For simplicity, assume there are $N = 1000$ patient records from which a simple random sample of $n = 20$ is to be drawn. We know that a simple random sample will be obtained if every possible sample of $n = 20$ records has the same chance of being selected. The digits in Table 3 of the Appendix, and in any other table of random numbers, are generated to satisfy the conditions of simple random sampling. Determine which records are to be included in a sample of size $n = 20$.

Solution

We can think of the accounts as being numbered 001, 002, ..., 999, 000. That is, we have 1000 three-digit numbers, where 001 represents the first record, 999 the 999th patient record, and 000 the 1000th.

Refer to Table 3 of the Appendix and use the first column; if we drop the last two digits of each number, we see that the first three-digit number formed is 104, the second is 223, the third is 241, and so on. Taking a random sample of 20 digits, we obtain the numbers shown in Table 4.1.

Table 4.1   Patient records to be included in the sample.

104	963	071
223	895	510
241	854	023
421	289	010
375	635	521
779	094	070
995	103	

If the records are actually numbered, we merely choose the records with the corresponding numbers, and these represent a simple random sample of $n = 20$ from $N = 1000$. If the patient accounts are not numbered, we can refer to a list of the accounts and count from the first to the 10th, 23rd, 70th, etc. until the desired numbers are reached. If a random number occurs twice, the second occurrence is omitted and another number is selected as its replacement.

4.3   Estimation of a Population Mean and Total

We stated previously that the objective of survey sampling is to draw inferences about a population based on information contained in a sample. One way to make inferences is to estimate certain population parameters by utilizing the sample information. The objective of a sample survey is often to estimate a population mean, denoted by μ, or a population total, denoted by τ. Thus, the auditor of Example 4.1 might be interested in the mean dollar value for the accounts receivable or the total dollar amount in these accounts. Hence, we consider estimation of the two population parameters, μ and τ, in this section.

Suppose that a simple random sample of n accounts is drawn, and we are to estimate the mean value per account for the total population of hospital records. Intuitively, we would employ the sample average,

$$\bar{y} = \frac{\sum\limits_{i=1}^{n} y_i}{n}$$

to estimate μ.

Of course, a single value of $\bar{y}$ tells us very little about the population mean, μ, unless we are able to evaluate the goodness of our estimator. Hence, in addition to estimating μ, we would like to place a bound on the error of estimation. It can be shown that $\bar{y}$ possesses many desirable properties for estimating μ. It is an unbiased estimator of μ; that is,

$$E(\bar{y}) = \mu. \tag{4.1}$$

The variance of the estimator, $\bar{y}$, is the same as that given in an introductory course except that it is multiplied by a correction factor to adjust for sampling from a finite population. The correction factor takes into account the fact that an estimate based on a sample $n = 10$ from a population of $N = 20$ items contains more information about the population than a sample of $n = 10$ from a population of $N = 20,000$.

Estimator of the population mean μ:

$$\hat{\mu} = \bar{y} = \frac{\sum\limits_{i=1}^{n} y_i}{n}. \tag{4.2}$$

Estimated variance of $\bar{y}$:

$$\hat{V}(\bar{y}) = \frac{s^2}{n}\left(\frac{N-n}{N}\right), \tag{4.3}$$

where

$$s^2 = \frac{\sum\limits_{i=1}^{n}(y_i - \bar{y})^2}{n-1}.$$

Bound on the error of estimation:

$$2\sqrt{\hat{V}(\bar{y})} = 2\sqrt{\frac{s^2}{n}\left(\frac{N-n}{N}\right)}. \tag{4.4}$$

The quantity $(N - n)/N$ is called the finite population correction (*fpc*). Note that this correction factor differs slightly from the one encountered in the true variance of $\bar{y}$. When n remains small relative to the population size N, the *fpc* is close to unity. Practically speaking, the *fpc* can be ignored if $(N - n)/N \geq .95$, or, equivalently, $n \leq (1/20)N$. In that case the estimated variance of $\bar{y}$ is the more familiar quantity s^2/n.

Example 4.2

Refer to the hospital audit of Example 4.1 and suppose that a random sample of $n = 200$ accounts is selected from the total of $N = 1000$. The sample mean of the accounts is found to be $\bar{y} = \$94.22$, and the sample variance is $s^2 = 445.21$. Estimate μ, the average due for all 1000 hospital accounts, and place a bound on the error of estimation.

Solution

We use $\bar{y} = \$94.22$ to estimate μ. A bound on the error of estimation can be found by using equation (4.4).

$$2\sqrt{\hat{V}(\bar{y})} = 2\sqrt{\frac{s^2}{n}\left(\frac{N-n}{N}\right)}$$

$$= 2\sqrt{\frac{445.21}{200}\left(\frac{1000-200}{1000}\right)}$$

$$= 2\sqrt{1.7808}$$

$$= \$2.67.$$

Thus, we estimate the mean value per account, μ, to be $\bar{y} = \$94.22$. By Tchebysheff's Theorem, at least 3/4 of the sample means differ from μ by less than two standard deviations of $\bar{y}$ in repeated sampling. Hence, we are reasonably confident that the error of estimation is less than $\$2.67$.

Example 4.3

A simple random sample of $n = 9$ hospital records is drawn to estimate the average amount of money due on $N = 484$ open accounts. The sample values for these nine records are listed in Table 4.2.
Estimate μ, the average amount outstanding, and place a bound on your error of estimation.

Table 4.2   Amount of money owed.

y_1	33.50
y_2	32.00
y_3	52.00
y_4	43.00
y_5	40.00
y_6	41.00
y_7	45.00
y_8	42.50
y_9	39.00

Solution

It is convenient to display the sample data and computations as indicated in Table 4.3.

Table 4.3   Data and computations for Example 4.3

y	y^2
33.50	1122.25
32.00	1024.00
52.00	2704.00
43.00	1849.00
40.00	1600.00
41.00	1681.00
45.00	2025.00
42.50	1806.25
39.00	1521.00
$\sum y_i = 368.00$	$\sum y_i^2 = 15332.50$

Summing the entries in the y column, we get

$$\sum_{i=1}^{9} y_i = 368.00.$$

Using the y^2 column, we have

$$\sum_{i=1}^{9} y_i^2 = 15332.50.$$

We need both of these quantities to calculate $\bar{y}$ and s^2. Our estimate of μ is

$$\bar{y} = \frac{\sum_{i=1}^{9} y_i}{9} = \frac{368.00}{9} = \$40.89.$$

To find a bound on the error of estimation we must compute

$$s^2 = \frac{\sum\limits_{i=1}^{n}(y_i - \bar{y})^2}{n-1}$$

$$= \frac{\sum\limits_{i=1}^{9}y_i^2 - \dfrac{\left(\sum\limits_{i=1}^{9}y_i\right)^2}{9}}{8} = \frac{1}{8}\left\{15332.50 - \frac{(368)^2}{9}\right\}$$

$$= \frac{1}{8}\{15332.50 - 15047.11\} = 35.67.$$

Utilizing equation (4.4), we obtain the bound on the error of estimation,

$$2\sqrt{\hat{V}(\bar{y})} = 2\sqrt{\frac{s^2}{n}\left(\frac{N-n}{N}\right)}$$

$$= 2\sqrt{\frac{35.67}{9}\left(\frac{484-9}{484}\right)} = 2\sqrt{3.890}$$

$$= 3.944 \quad (\text{i.e., } \$3.94).$$

To summarize, the estimate of the mean amount of money owed per account, μ, is $\bar{y} = \$40.89$. Although we cannot be certain how close $\bar{y}$ is to μ, we are reasonably confident that the error of estimation is less than $3.94.

Many sample surveys are conducted to obtain information about a population total. The federal auditor of Example 4.1 would probably be interested in verifying the computer figure for the total accounts receivable (in dollars) for the $N = 1000$ open accounts.

You recall that the mean for a population of size N is the sum of all observations in the population divided by N. Symbolically we can represent μ as

$$\mu = \frac{\sum\limits_{i=1}^{N} y_i}{N}.$$

The population total, i.e., the sum of all observations in the population, is denoted by the symbol τ. Hence,

$$\sum\limits_{i=1}^{N} y_i = N\mu = \tau.$$

Intuitively, we expect the estimator of τ to be N times the estimator of μ. In fact this is the case.

Estimator of the population total τ:

$$\hat{\tau} = N\bar{y} = \frac{N \sum\limits_{i=1}^{n} y_i}{n}.$$ (4.5)

Estimated variance of $\hat{\tau}$:

$$\hat{V}(\hat{\tau}) = \hat{V}(N\bar{y}) = N^2 \frac{s^2}{n} \left(\frac{N-n}{N} \right),$$ (4.6)

where

$$s^2 = \frac{\sum\limits_{i=1}^{n}(y_i - \bar{y})^2}{n-1}.$$

Bound on the error of estimation:

$$2\sqrt{\hat{V}(N\bar{y})} = 2\sqrt{N^2 \frac{s^2}{n} \left(\frac{N-n}{N} \right)}.$$ (4.7)

The reader should note that the estimated variance of $\hat{\tau} = N\bar{y}$ in equation (4.6) is N^2 times the estimated variance of $\bar{y}$ given in equation (4.3).

Example 4.4

An industrial firm is concerned about the time per week spent by scientists on certain trivial tasks. The time log sheets of a simple random sample of $n = 50$ employees show the average amount of time spent on these tasks is 10.31 hours with a sample variance $s^2 = 2.25$. If the company employs $N = 750$ scientists, estimate the total number of man hours lost per week on trivial tasks, and place a bound on the error of estimation.

Solution

We know the population consists of $N = 750$ employees from which a random sample of $n = 50$ time log sheets was obtained. The average amount of time lost for the fifty employees was $\bar{y} = 10.31$ hours per week. Therefore, the estimate of τ is

$$\hat{\tau} = N\bar{y} = 750(10.31) = 7732.5 \text{ hours.}$$

To place a bound on the error of estimation, we apply equation (4.7) to obtain

$$2\sqrt{\hat{V}(\hat{\tau})} = 2\sqrt{(750)^2\left(\frac{2.25}{50}\right)\left(\frac{750-50}{750}\right)}$$

$$= 2\sqrt{23,625}$$

$$= 307.4 \text{ hours.}$$

Thus, the estimate of total time lost is $\hat{\tau} = 7732.5$ hours. We are reasonably confident that the error of estimation is less than 307.4 hours.

4.4   Selecting the Sample Size for Estimating Population Means and Totals

At some point in the design of the survey, someone must make a decision about the size of the sample to be selected from the population. So far, we have discussed a sampling procedure (simple random sampling) but have said nothing about the number of observations to be included in the sample. The implications of such a decision are obvious. Observations cost money. Hence, if the sample is too large, time and talent are wasted. Conversely, if the number of observations included in the sample is too small, we have bought inadequate information for the time and effort expended and have again been wasteful.

The number of observations needed to estimate a population mean, μ, with a bound on the error of estimation of magnitude B is found by setting two standard deviations of the estimator, $\bar{y}$, equal to B and solving this expression for n. That is, we must solve

$$2\sqrt{V(\bar{y})} = B \tag{4.8}$$

for n.

Although we have not discussed the form of $V(\bar{y})$, you will recall that the estimated variance of $\bar{y}$, $\hat{V}(\bar{y})$ is given by

$$\hat{V}(\bar{y}) = \frac{s^2}{n}\left(\frac{N-n}{N}\right). \tag{4.9}$$

The corresponding population variance of $\bar{y}$, $V(\bar{y})$, is similar to $\hat{V}(\bar{y})$ except that the finite population correction factor is $(N-n)/(N-1)$. Thus,

$$V(\bar{y}) = \frac{\sigma^2}{n}\left(\frac{N-n}{(N-1)}\right). \tag{4.10}$$

You will recognize equation (4.10) from an introductory course as the familiar variance of $\bar{y}$, that is, σ^2/n, multiplied by the finite population correction factor, $(N-n)/(N-1)$.

The required sample size can now be found by solving the following equation for n:

$$2\sqrt{V(\bar{y})} = 2\sqrt{\frac{\sigma^2}{n} \cdot \frac{N-n}{N-1}} = B. \tag{4.11}$$

The solution is given in equation (4.12).

Sample size required to estimate μ with a bound on the error of estimation B:

$$n = \frac{N\sigma^2}{(N-1)D + \sigma^2}, \tag{4.12}$$

where

$$D = \frac{B^2}{4}.$$

Solving for **n** in a practical situation presents a problem because the population variance, σ^2, is unknown. Since a sample variance, s^2, is frequently available from prior experimentation, we can obtain an approximate sample size by replacing σ^2 with s^2 in equation (4.12). We will illustrate a method for guessing a value of σ^2 when very little prior information is available.

Example 4.5

It is necessary to estimate the average amount of money, μ, for a hospital's accounts receivable. Although no prior data is available to estimate the population variance, σ^2, it is known that most accounts lie within a \$100 range. If there are $N = 1000$ open accounts, find the sample size needed to estimate μ with a bound on the error of estimation, $B = \$3$.

Solution

We need an estimate of σ^2, the population variance. Since the range is approximately equal to 4 standard deviations (4σ) by the Empirical Rule, one-fourth of the range will provide an approximate value of σ. Hence,

$$\sigma \approx \frac{\text{range}}{4} = \frac{100}{4} = 25,$$

and

$$\sigma^2 \approx (25)^2 = 625.$$

Using equation (4.12), we obtain

$$n = \frac{N\sigma^2}{(N-1)D + \sigma^2}, \quad \text{where} \;\; D = \frac{B^2}{4} = \frac{(3)^2}{4} = 2.25,$$

$$= \frac{1000(625)}{999(2.25) + 625} = 217.56.$$

That is, we need approximately 218 observations to estimate μ, the mean accounts receivable, with a bound on the error of estimation of \$3.00.

In like manner, we can determine the number of observations needed to estimate a population total, τ, with a bound on the error of estimation of magnitude B. The required sample size is found by setting two standard deviations of the estimator, $N\bar{y}$, equal to B and solving this expression for n. That is, we must solve

$$2\sqrt{V(N\bar{y})} = B$$

or, equivalently,

$$2N\sqrt{V(\bar{y})} = B. \qquad (4.13)$$

(The reason for this equivalence is given directly after equation (4.7).)

The sample size required to estimate τ with a bound on error B:

$$n = \frac{N\sigma^2}{(N-1)D + \sigma^2},\qquad (4.14)$$

where

$$D = \frac{B^2}{4N^2}.$$

Example 4.6

An investigator is interested in estimating the total weight gain in 0 to 4 weeks for $N = 1000$ chicks fed on a new ration. Obviously it would be time consuming and tedious to weigh each bird. Therefore, determine the number of chicks to be sampled in this study in order to estimate τ with a bound on the error of estimation equal to 1000 grams. Many similar studies on chick nutrition have been run in the past. Using data from these studies, the investigator found that σ^2, the population variance, was approximately equal to 36.00 grams. Determine the required sample size.

Solution

We can obtain an approximate sample size using equation (4.14) with σ^2 equal to 36.00 and

$$D = \frac{B^2}{4N^2} = \frac{(1000)^2}{4(1000)^2} = 0.25.$$

That is,

$$n = \frac{N\sigma^2}{(N-1)D + \sigma^2} = \frac{1000(36.00)}{999(0.25) + 36.00} = 125.98.$$

The investigator, therefore, needs to weigh $n = 126$ chicks to estimate τ, the total weight gain for $N = 1000$ chickens in 0 to 4 weeks, with a bound on the error of estimation equal to 1000 grams.

4.5   Estimation of a Population Proportion

The investigator conducting a sample survey is frequently interested in estimating the proportion of the population which possesses a specified characteristic. For example, a congressional leader investigating the merits of an
eighteen-year-old voting age might want to estimate the proportion of the
potential voters in his district between the ages of eighteen and twenty-one. A
marketing research group might be interested in the proportion of the total
sales market in diet preparations which is attributable to a particular product.
That is, what percentage of sales is accounted for by a particular product? A
forest manager might be interested in the proportion of trees with a diameter of
12 inches or more. Television ratings are often determined by estimating the
proportion of the viewing public that watches a particular program.

You will recognize that all of these examples exhibit a characteristic of the
binomial experiment, i.e., an observation either does belong or does not belong
to the category of interest. For example, one could estimate the proportion of
eligible voters in a particular district by examining population census data for
several of the precincts within the district. An estimate of the proportion of
voters between eighteen and twenty-one years of age for the entire district would
be the fraction of potential voters from the precincts sampled that fell into this
age range.

In subsequent discussion, we denote the population proportion and its estimator by the symbols p and $\hat{p}$, respectively. The properties of $\hat{p}$ for simple
random sampling parallel those of the sample mean, $\bar{y}$, if the response measurements are defined as follows: let $y_i = 0$ if the ith element sampled does not
possess the specified characteristic and $y_i = 1$ if it does. Then the total number
of elements in a sample of size n possessing a specified characteristic is

$$\sum_{i=1}^{n} y_i.$$

If we draw a simple random sample of size n, the sample proportion $\hat{p}$ would
be the fraction of the elements in the sample that possess the characteristic of
interest. For example, the estimate $\hat{p}$ of the proportion of eligible voters between
the ages of 18 and 21 in a certain district would be

$$\hat{p} = \frac{\text{number of voters sampled between the ages of 18 and 21}}{\text{number of voters sampled}},$$

or

$$\hat{p} = \frac{\sum_{i=1}^{n} y_i}{n} = \bar{y}.$$

In other words, $\hat{p}$ is the average of the 0 and 1 values from the sample. Similarly, we can think of the population proportion as the average of the 0 and 1 values for the entire population (i.e., $p = \mu$).

Estimator of the population proportion p:

$$\hat{p} = \bar{y} = \frac{\sum_{i=1}^{n} y_i}{n}. \qquad (4.15)$$

Estimated variance of $\hat{p}$:

$$\hat{V}(\hat{p}) = \frac{\hat{p}\hat{q}}{(n-1)} \left(\frac{N-n}{N} \right), \qquad (4.16)$$

where

$$\hat{q} = 1 - \hat{p}.$$

Bound on the error of estimation:

$$2\sqrt{\hat{V}(\hat{p})} = 2\sqrt{\frac{\hat{p}\hat{q}}{n-1} \left(\frac{N-n}{N} \right)}. \qquad (4.17)$$

Example 4.7

A simple random sample of $n = 100$ college seniors was selected to estimate (1), the fraction of $N = 300$ seniors going on to graduate school and (2), the fraction of students that have held part-time jobs during college. Let y_i and x_i ($i = 1, 2, \ldots, 100$) denote the responses of the ith student sampled. We will set $y_i = 0$ if the ith student does not plan to attend graduate school and $y_i = 1$ if he does. Similarly, let $x_i = 0$ if he has not held a part-time job sometime during college and $x_i = 1$ if he has. Using the sample data presented below, estimate p_1, the proportion of seniors planning to attend graduate school, and p_2, the proportion of seniors who have had a part-time job sometime during their college careers (summers included).

Student	y	x
1	1	0
2	0	1
3	0	1
4	1	1
5	0	0
6	0	0
7	0	1
$\vdots$	$\vdots$	$\vdots$
96	0	1
97	1	0
98	0	1
99	0	1
100	1	1

$$\sum_{i=1}^{100} y_i = 15 \qquad \sum_{i=1}^{100} x_i = 65$$

Solution

The sample proportions from equation (4.15) are given by

$$\hat{p}_1 = \frac{\sum_{i=1}^{n} y_i}{n} = \frac{15}{100} = .15,$$

and

$$\hat{p}_2 = \frac{\sum_{i=1}^{n} x_i}{n} = \frac{65}{100} = .65.$$

The bounds on the errors of estimation of p_1 and p_2 are, respectively,

$$2\sqrt{\hat{V}(\hat{p}_1)} = 2\sqrt{\frac{\hat{p}_1 \hat{q}_1}{n-1}\left(\frac{N-n}{N}\right)}$$

$$= 2\sqrt{\frac{(.15)(.85)}{99}\left(\frac{300-100}{300}\right)}$$

$$= 2(.0293) = .059,$$

and

$$2\sqrt{\hat{V}(\hat{p}_2)} = 2\sqrt{\frac{\hat{p}_2\hat{q}_2}{n-1}\left(\frac{N-n}{N}\right)}$$

$$= 2\sqrt{\frac{(.65)(.35)}{99}\left(\frac{300-100}{300}\right)}$$

$$= 2(.0391) = .078.$$

Thus, we estimate that .15 (15%) of the seniors plan to attend graduate school, with a bound on the error of estimation equal to .059 (5.9%). Similarly, we estimate that .65 (65%) of the seniors have held a part-time job during college, with a bound on the error of estimation equal to .078 (7.8%).

We have shown that the population proportion, p, can be regarded as the average (μ) of the zero and one values for the entire binomial population. Hence, the problem of determining the sample size required to estimate p to within B units should be analogous to determining a sample size for estimating μ with a bound on the error of estimation, B. You will recall that the required sample size for estimating μ is given by

$$n = \frac{N\sigma^2}{(N-1)D + \sigma^2},\tag{4.18}$$

where $D = B^2/4$ (see equation 4.12).

The corresponding sample size needed to estimate p can be found by replacing σ^2 in equation (4.18) with the quantity pq.

Sample size required to estimate p with a bound on the error of estimation, B:

$$n = \frac{Npq}{(N-1)D + pq},\tag{4.19}$$

where

$$q = 1 - p \quad\text{and}\quad D = \frac{B^2}{4}.$$

In a practical situation, one does not know p. An approximate sample size can be found by replacing p with an estimated value. Frequently such an estimate can be obtained from similar past surveys. However, if no such prior information is available, one can substitute $p = .5$ into equation (4.19) to obtain a conservative sample size (one that is likely to be larger than required).

Example 4.8

Student government leaders at a college want to conduct a survey to determine the proportion of students which favors a proposed honor code. Since it is almost impossible to interview $N = 2000$ students in a reasonable length of time, determine the sample size (number of students to be interviewed) needed to estimate p with a bound on the error of estimation of magnitude $B = .05$. Assume that no prior information is available to estimate p.

Solution

We can approximate the required sample sizes when no prior information is available by setting $p = .5$ in equation (4.19). We have

$$D = \frac{B^2}{4} = \frac{(.05)^2}{4} = .000625.$$

Hence,

$$n = \frac{Npq}{(N-1)D + pq}$$

$$= \frac{(2000)(.5)(.5)}{(1999)(.000625) + (.5)(.5)} = \frac{500}{1.499}$$

$$= 333.56.$$

That is, 334 students must be interviewed to estimate the proportion of students which favors the proposed honor code with a bound on the error of estimation, $B = .05$.

Example 4.9

Referring to Example 4.8, suppose that in addition to estimating the proportion of students which favors the proposed honor code, student government leaders also want to estimate the number of students who feel the student union building adequately serves their needs. Determine the combined sample size required for a survey to estimate p_1, the proportion which favors the proposed honor code, and p_2, the proportion which believes the student union adequately serves its needs, with bounds on the errors of estimation of magnitude $B_1 = .05$ and $B_2 = .07$, respectively. Although no prior information is available to estimate p_1, approximately 60% of the students believed the union adequately met their needs in a similar survey run the previous year.

Solution

In this example, we must determine a sample size, n, which will allow us to estimate p_1 with a bound $B_1 = .05$ and p_2 with a bound $B_2 = .07$. First, we determine the sample sizes which satisfy each objective separately. The larger of the two will then be the combined sample size for a survey to meet both objectives. From Example 4.8, the sample size required to estimate p_1 with a bound on the error of estimation of $B_1 = .05$ was $n = 334$ students. We can use data from the survey of the previous year to determine the sample size needed to estimate p_2. We have

$$D = \frac{B^2}{4} = \frac{(.07)^2}{4} = .001225,$$

and hence, using $p_2 = .60$,

$$n = \frac{Npq}{(N-1)D + pq}$$

$$= \frac{(2000)(.6)(.4)}{(1999)(.001225) + (.6)(.4)} = \frac{480}{2.68877}$$

$$= 178.52.$$

That is, 179 students must be interviewed to estimate p_2, the proportion of the $N = 2000$ students which believes the student union meets its needs, with a bound on the error of estimation equal to .07.

The sample size required to achieve both objectives in one survey is 334, the larger of the two sample sizes.

4.6   Summary

The objective of statistics is to make inferences about a population based on information contained in a sample. Two factors affect the quantity of information in a given investigation. The first is the sample size. The larger the sample size, the more information we expect to obtain about the population. The second factor which affects the quantity of information is the amount of variation in the data. This can be controlled by the design of the sample survey; that is, the method by which observations are obtained.

In this chapter we discussed the simplest type of sample survey design, namely, simple random sampling. This design does not attempt to reduce the effect of data variation on the error of estimation. A simple random sample of size n occurs if each sample of n elements from the population has the same chance of being selected. Random number tables are quite useful in determining the elements that are to be included in a simple random sample.

In estimating a population mean, μ, and total, τ, we use the sample mean, $\bar{y}$, and sample total, $N\bar{y}$, respectively. Both estimators are unbiased; that is, $E(\bar{y}) = \mu$ and $E(N\bar{y}) = \tau$. The estimated variance and bound on the error of estimation are given for both estimators.

Sometime during the design of an actual survey, the experimenter must decide how much information is desired; that is, how large a bound on the error of estimation can be tolerated. Sample size requirements were presented for estimating μ and τ with a specified bound on the error of estimation.

The third parameter estimated was the population proportion, p. The properties of $\hat{p}$ were presented and related to the properties of $\bar{y}$, the estimator of the population mean, μ. Selecting the sample size to estimate p with a specified bound on the error of estimation was based on the same principle employed in selecting a sample size for estimating μ and τ.

References

Cochran, W. G., *Sampling Techniques*, 2d ed., New York: John Wiley and Sons, Inc., 1963.

Hansen, M. H., W. N. Hurwitz, and W. G. Madow, *Sample Survey Methods and Theory*, Vol. 1. New York: John Wiley and Sons, Inc., 1953.

Kish, L., *Survey Sampling*, New York: John Wiley and Sons, Inc., 1965.

Exercises

4.1   State park officials were interested in the proportion of campers who consider the campsite spacing adequate in a particular campground. They decided to take a simple random sample of $n = 30$ from the first $N = 300$ camping parties which visit the campground. Let $y_i = 0$ if the head of the ith party sampled does not think the spacing is adequate and $y_i = 1$ if he does ($i = 1, 2, \ldots, 30$). Use the data below to estimate p, the proportion of campers who consider the campsite spacing adequate. Place a bound on the error of estimation.

Camper sampled	Response y_i
1	1
2	0
3	1
⋮	⋮
29	1
30	1

$$\sum_{i=1}^{30} y_i = 25$$

4.2   Use the data in Exercise 4.1 to determine the sample size required to estimate p with a bound on the error of estimation of magnitude $B = .05$.

4.3   A simple random sample of 100 water meters within a community is monitored to estimate the average daily water consumption per household over a specified dry spell. The sample mean and sample variance are found to be $\bar{y} = 12.5$ and $s^2 = 1252$, respectively. If we assume that there are $N = 10,000$ households within the community, estimate μ, the true average daily consumption, and place a bound on the error of estimation.

4.4   Using Exercise 4.3, estimate the total number of gallons of water, τ, used daily during the dry spell. Place a bound on the error of estimation.

4.5   Resource managers of forest game lands are concerned about the size of the deer and rabbit populations during the winter months in a particular forest. As an estimate of population size, they propose using the average number of pellet groups for rabbits and deer per 30 foot square plots. Using an aerial photograph, the forest was divided into $N = 10,000$ thirty foot square grids. A simple random sample of $n = 500$ plots was taken, and the number of pellet groups was observed for rabbits and for deer. The results of this study are summarized below:

Deer	Rabbits
Sample mean = 2.30	Sample mean = 4.52
Sample variance = 0.65	Sample variance = 0.97

Estimate μ_1 and μ_2, the average number of pellet groups for deer and rabbits respectively, per 30 square foot plots. Place bounds on the errors of estimation.

4.6   A simple random sample of $n = 40$ college students was interviewed to determine the proportion of students in favor of converting from the semester to the quarter system. If 25 of the students answered affirmatively, estimate the proportion of students on campus in favor of the change. (Assume $N = 2,000$.) Place a bound on the error of estimation.

4.7   A dentist was interested in the effectiveness of a new toothpaste. A group of $N = 1,000$ school children participated in a study. Prestudy records showed there was an average of 2.2 cavities every six months for the group. After three months on the study, the dentist sampled $n = 10$ children to determine how they were progressing on the new toothpaste. Using the data below, estimate the mean number of cavities for the entire group and place a bound on the error of estimation.

Child	Number of cavities in the three-month period
1	0
2	4
3	2
4	3
5	2
6	0
7	3
8	4
9	1
10	1

4.8   The Fish and Game department of a particular state was concerned about the direction of its future hunting programs. In order to provide for a greater potential for future hunting, the department wanted to determine the proportion of hunters seeking any type of game bird. A simple random sample of $n = 1000$ of the $N = 99,000$ licensed hunters was obtained. If 430 indicated they hunted game birds, estimate p, the proportion of licensed hunters seeking game birds. Place a bound on the error of estimation.

4.9   Using the data in Exercise 4.8, determine the sample size the department must obtain to estimate the proportion of game-bird hunters, given a bound on the error of estimation of magnitude $B = .02$.

4.10 A company auditor was interested in estimating the total number of travel vouchers that were incorrectly filed. In a simple random sample of $n = 50$ vouchers taken from a group of $N = 250$, 20 were filed incorrectly. Estimate the total number of vouchers from the $N = 250$ that have been filed incorrectly, and place a bound on the error of estimation. (*Hint:* If p is the population proportion of incorrect vouchers, then Np is the total number of incorrect vouchers. An estimator of Np is $N\hat{p}$ which has an estimated variance given by $N^2\hat{V}(\hat{p})$.)

4.11 A psychologist wishes to estimate the average reaction time to a stimulus among 200 patients in a hospital specializing in nervous disorders. A simple random sample of $n = 20$ patients was selected and their reaction times were measured with the following results:

$$\bar{y} = 2.1 \text{ seconds}, \qquad s = .4 \text{ second}.$$

Estimate the population mean, μ, and place a bound on the error of estimation.

4.12   In Exercise 4.11, how large a sample should be taken in order to estimate μ with a bound of one second on the error of estimation? Use 1.0 second as an approximation of the population standard deviation.

4.13   The manager of a machine shop wishes to estimate the average time that it takes for an operator to complete a simple task. The shop has 98 operators. Eight operators are selected at random and timed. The following are the observed results:

Time in minutes

4.2	5.3
5.1	4.6
7.9	5.1
3.8	4.1

Estimate the average time for completion of the task among all operators, and place a bound on the error of estimation.

4.14   A sociological study conducted in a small town calls for the estimation of the proportion of households which contain at least one member over 65 years of age. The city has 621 households according to the most recent city directory. A simple random sample of $n = 60$ households was selected from the directory. At the completion of the field work, out of the 60 households sampled, 11 contained at least one member over 65 years of age. Estimate the true population proportion, p, and place a bound on the error of estimation.

4.15   In Exercise 4.14, how large a sample should be taken in order to estimate p with a bound of .08 on the error of estimation? Assume the true proportion p is approximately .2.

4.16   An investigator is interested in estimating the total number of "count trees" (trees larger than a specified size) on a plantation of $N = 1500$ acres. This information is used to determine the total volume of lumber for trees on the plantation. A simple random sample of $n = 100$ one-acre plots was selected, and each plot was examined for the number of count trees. If the sample average for the $n = 100$ one-acre plots was $\bar{y} = 25.2$ with a sample variance of $s^2 = 136$, estimate the total number of count trees on the plantation. Place a bound on the error of estimation.

4.17   Using the results of the survey conducted in Exercise 4.16, determine the sample size required to estimate τ, the total number of trees on the plantation, with a bound on the error of estimation of magnitude $B = 1500$.

5

Stratified Random Sampling

5.1 Introduction

The purpose of sample survey design is to maximize the amount of information for a given cost. Simple random sampling, the basic sampling design, often provides good estimates of population quantities at low cost. In this chapter we define a second sampling procedure, stratified random sampling, which in many instances increases the quantity of information for a given cost.

Definition 5.1 A *stratified random sample* is one obtained by separating the population elements into nonoverlapping groups, called *strata*, and then selecting a simple random sample from each stratum.

A public opinion poll is to be conducted over a state which contains two large cities and a rural area. The elements in the population of interest are all the men and women over 21 years of age in the state. A stratified random sample from this state could be obtained by selecting a simple random sample of adults from each city and another simple random sample from the rural area. That is, the two cities and the rural area represent three separate strata from which we obtain simple random samples.

There are three reasons stratified random sampling often results in increased information for a given cost:

1. The data should be more homogeneous within each stratum than in the population as a whole.
2. The cost of conducting the actual sampling tends to be less for stratified random sampling than for simple random sampling because of administrative convenience.
3. When stratified sampling is used, separate estimates of population parameters can be obtained for each stratum without additional sampling.

Reduced variability within each stratum produces stratified sampling estimators which have smaller variances than do the corresponding simple random sampling estimators from the same sample size.

Each stratum has fewer people and covers a smaller geographic area than does the whole population. Therefore, it is more convenient to choose the samples and to collect the data in the smaller strata. Also, separate teams of investigators can work in each stratum and hence the survey can be completed more quickly.

In the above example, each of the cities in the public opinion poll could be surveyed by using the simple random sample from that stratum and by following methods set forth in Chapter 4.

5.2   How to Draw a Stratified Random Sample

The first step in the selection of a stratified random sample is to clearly specify the strata; then we place each sampling unit of the population into its appropriate stratum. This may be more difficult than it sounds. For example, suppose that you plan to stratify the sampling units, say households, into rural and urban units. What should be done with households in a town of 1000 inhabitants? Are these households rural or urban? They may be rural if the town is isolated in the country, or they may be urban if the town is adjacent to a large city. Hence, it is essential to specify what is meant by urban and rural so that each sampling unit clearly falls into only one stratum.

After the sampling units are divided into strata, one selects a simple random sample from each stratum by using the techniques given in Chapter 4. We discuss the problem of choosing appropriate sample sizes for the strata later in this chapter. One must be certain that the samples selected from the strata are independent. That is, different random sampling schemes should be used within each stratum so that the observations chosen in one stratum do not depend upon those chosen in another.

The following example illustrates the problem of estimating a population mean from a stratified random sample.

Example 5.1

An advertising firm is interested in determining how much to emphasize television advertising in a given county. The firm decides to conduct a sample survey to estimate the average number of hours per week that households in the county watch television (that is, the average number of hours per week the television set is actually turned on). Suggest a survey design for this problem.

Solution

The county contains two towns. Therefore, the households in this county are grouped into three distinct segments, town A, town B, and the surrounding rural area. Town A is built around a factory, and most of the households contain factory workers with school-age children. Town B is an exclusive suburb of a city in a neighboring county and contains older people with few children at home. A stratified random sample with three strata appears to be an appropriate sample survey design because of administrative conveniences and similarities in behavior patterns within each group. We would expect small variability within each stratum.

Let L denote the number of strata, N_i the number of sampling units in stratum i, and N the number of sampling units in the population. Then $N = N_1 + N_2 + \cdots + N_L$. For Example 5.1, $N_1 = 155$ households in town A, $N_2 = 62$ in town B, and $N_3 = 93$ rural households; therefore, $N = 310$ households in the population.

The advertising firm has enough time and money to interview only $n = 40$ households, and it decides to select random samples of size $n_1 = 20$ from town A, $n_2 = 8$ from town B, and $n_3 = 12$ from the rural area. (We shall give the reason for choosing unequal sample sizes later.) The simple random samples are selected and the interviews conducted. The results of the survey are shown in Table 5.1.

Table 5.1   Television Viewing Time in Hours per Week

Stratum 1—Town A	Stratum 2—Town B	Stratum 3—Rural Area
35 28 26 41	27 4 49 10	8 15 21 7
43 29 32 37	15 41 25 30	14 30 20 11
36 25 29 31		12 32 34 24
39 38 40 45		
28 27 35 34		

Table 5.2   Calculations for Table 5.1

Stratum 1	Stratum 2	Stratum 3
$n_1 = 20$	$n_2 = 8$	$n_3 = 12$
$\bar{y}_1 = 33.900$	$\bar{y}_2 = 25.125$	$\bar{y}_3 = 19.000$
$s_1^2 = 35.358$	$s_2^2 = 232.411$	$s_3^2 = 87.636$
$N_1 = 155$	$N_2 = 62$	$N_3 = 93$

The terms s_1^2, s_2^2, and s_3^2 in Table 5.2 are the sample variances for strata 1, 2, and 3, respectively; they are given by the formula

$$s_i^2 = \frac{\sum_{i=1}^{n_i}(y_{ij} - \bar{y}_i)^2}{n_i - 1}, \quad i = 1, 2, 3,$$

where y_{ij} is the jth observation in stratum i. These variances estimate the corresponding true stratum variances σ_1^2, σ_2^2, and σ_3^2.

5.3   Estimation of a Population Mean and Total

How can we use the data of Table 5.1 to estimate the population mean? Let $\bar{y}_i$ denote the sample mean for the simple random sample selected from stratum i, μ_i the population mean for stratum i, and τ_i the population total for stratum i. Then the population total, τ, is equal to $\tau_1 + \tau_2 + \cdots + \tau_L$. We have a simple random sample within each stratum. Therefore, we know from Chapter 4 that $\bar{y}_i$ is an unbiased estimator of μ_i and $N_i \bar{y}_i$ is an unbiased estimator of the stratum total $\tau_i = N_i \mu_i$. It seems reasonable to form an estimator of τ, which is the sum of the τ_i's, by summing the estimators of the τ_i's. Similarly, since the population mean, μ, equals the population total, τ, divided by N, an unbiased estimator of μ is obtained by summing the estimators of the τ_i's over all strata and then dividing by N. We denote this estimator by $\bar{y}_{st}$, where the subscript "st" indicates that stratified random sampling is used.

Estimator of the population mean μ:

$$\bar{y}_{st} = \frac{1}{N} [N_1 \bar{y}_1 + N_2 \bar{y}_2 + \cdots + N_L \bar{y}_L] = \frac{1}{N} \sum_{i=1}^{L} N_i \bar{y}_i. \qquad (5.1)$$

Estimated variance of $\bar{y}_{st}$:

$$\hat{V}(\bar{y}_{st}) = \frac{1}{N^2} [N_1^2 \hat{V}(\bar{y}_1) + N_2^2 \hat{V}(\bar{y}_2) + \cdots + N_L^2 \hat{V}(\bar{y}_L)]$$

$$= \frac{1}{N^2} \left[N_1^2 \left(\frac{N_1 - n_1}{N_1} \right) \frac{s_1^2}{n_1} + \cdots + N_L^2 \left(\frac{N_L - n_L}{N_L} \right) \frac{s_L^2}{n_L} \right]$$

$$= \frac{1}{N^2} \sum_{i=1}^{L} N_i^2 \left(\frac{N_i - n_i}{N_i} \right) \frac{s_i^2}{n_i}. \qquad (5.2)$$

Bound on the error of estimation:

$$2\sqrt{\hat{V}(\bar{y}_{st})} = 2\sqrt{\frac{1}{N^2} \sum_{i=1}^{L} \left(\frac{N_i - n_i}{N_i} \right) \frac{s_i^2}{n_i}} \qquad (5.3)$$

Example 5.2

Using the data in Table 5.1, estimate the average television viewing time (in hours per week) for:
(a) all households in the county,
(b) all households in town *B*.
In both cases place a bound on the error of estimation.

Solution

(a) From Table 5.1 and equation (5.1),

$$\bar{y}_{st} = \frac{1}{N} [N_1 \bar{y}_1 + N_2 \bar{y}_2 + N_3 \bar{y}_3]$$

$$= \frac{1}{310} [(155)(33.900) + (62)(25.125) + (93)(19.000)]$$

$$= 27.675$$

is the best estimate of the average number of hours per week spent watching television by all households in the county. Also,

$$\hat{V}(\bar{y}_{st}) = \frac{1}{N^2} \sum_{i=1}^{3} N_i^2 \left(\frac{N_i - n_i}{N_i} \right) \frac{s_i^2}{n_i}$$

$$= \frac{1}{(310)^2} \left[\frac{(155)^2(.871)\ 35.358}{20} + \frac{(62)^2(.871)(232.411)}{8} \right.$$

$$\left. + \frac{(93)^2(.871)(87.636)}{12} \right]$$

$$= 1.97.$$

The estimate of the population mean with an approximate two standard deviation bound on the error of estimation is given by

$$\bar{y}_{st} \pm 2\sqrt{\hat{V}(\bar{y}_{st})},$$

$$27.675 \pm 2\sqrt{1.97},$$

$$27.675 \pm (2.807).$$

Thus, we estimate the average number of hours per week that households in the county view television to be 27.675 hours. The error of estimation should be less than 2.807 hours with probability approximately equal to .95.

   (b) The $n_2 = 8$ observations from stratum 2 constitute a simple random sample; hence, we can apply formulas from Chapter 4. The estimate of the average viewing time for town B with an approximate two standard deviation bound on the error of estimation is given by

$$\bar{y}_2 \pm 2\sqrt{\left(\frac{N_2 - n_2}{N_2} \right) \frac{s_2^2}{n_2}},$$

$$25.125 \pm 2\sqrt{\left(\frac{62 - 8}{62} \right) \frac{232.411}{8}},$$

or

$$25.125 \pm 10.06.$$

This estimate has a large bound on the error of estimation because s_2^2 is large and the sample size, n_2, is small. Thus, the estimate $\bar{y}_{st}$ of the population mean is quite good but the estimate $\bar{y}_2$ of the mean of stratum 2 is poor. If an estimate is desired for a particular stratum, the sample from that stratum must be large enough to provide a reasonable bound on the error of estimation.

Procedures for the estimation of a population total, τ, follow directly from the procedures presented for estimating μ. Since τ is equal to $N\mu$, an unbiased estimator of τ is given by $N\bar{y}_{st}$.

Estimator of the population total τ:

$$N\bar{y}_{st} = N_1\bar{y}_1 + N_2\bar{y}_2 + \cdots + N_L\bar{y}_L = \sum_{i=1}^{L} N_i\bar{y}_i. \tag{5.4}$$

Estimated variance of $N\bar{y}_{st}$:

$$\hat{V}(N\bar{y}_{st}) = N^2\hat{V}(\bar{y}_{st}) = \sum_{i=1}^{L} N_i^2\left(\frac{N_i - n_i}{N_i}\right)\frac{s_i^2}{n_i}. \tag{5.5}$$

Bound on the error of estimation:

$$2\sqrt{\hat{V}(N\bar{y}_{st})} = 2\sqrt{\sum_{i=1}^{L} N_i^2\left(\frac{N_i - n_i}{N_i}\right)\frac{s_i^2}{n_i}}. \tag{5.6}$$

Example 5.3

Refer to Example 5.1 and estimate the total number of hours per week that households in the county view television. Place a bound on the error of estimation.

Solution

For the data in Table 5.1,

$$N\bar{y}_{st} = 310(27.675) = 8579.250 \text{ hours.}$$

The estimated variance of $N\bar{y}_{st}$ is given by

$$\hat{V}(N\bar{y}_{st}) = N^2\hat{V}(\bar{y}_{st}) = (310)^2(1.97) = 189,278.560.$$

The estimate of the population total with a bound on the error of estimation is given by

$$N\bar{y}_{st} \pm 2\sqrt{\hat{V}(N\bar{y}_{st})},$$

$$8579.25 \pm 2\sqrt{189,278.560},$$

$$8579.25 \pm 2(435.06),$$

or

$$8579.25 \pm 870.12.$$

Thus, we estimate the total weekly viewing time for households in the county to be 8,579.25 hours. The error of estimation should be less than 870.12 hours with probability equal to .95.

5.4   Selecting the Sample Size for Estimating Population Means and Totals

The amount of information in a sample depends on the sample size n, since $V(\bar{y}_{st})$ decreases as n increases. Let us examine a method of choosing the sample size to obtain a fixed amount of information for estimating a population parameter. Suppose the experimenter specifies that the estimate, $\bar{y}_{st}$, should lie within B units of the population mean, with probability approximately equal to .95. Symbolically, he wants

$$2\sqrt{V(\bar{y}_{st})} = B,$$

or

$$V(\bar{y}_{st}) = \frac{B^2}{4}.$$

The above equation contains the actual population variance of $\bar{y}_{st}$ rather than the estimated variance. The actual variance, $V(\bar{y}_{st})$, looks very similar to equation (5.2) with $s_1^2, s_2^2, \ldots, s_L^2$ replaced by $\sigma_1^2, \sigma_2^2, \ldots, \sigma_L^2$.

Although we set $V(\bar{y}_{st})$ equal to $B^2/4$, we cannot solve for n unless we know something about the relationships among $n_1, n_2, \ldots, n_L$ and n. There are many ways of allocating a sample of size n among the various strata. In each case, however, the number of observations n_i allocated to the ith stratum is some fraction of the total sample size n. We denote this fraction by w_i. Hence, we can write

$$n_i = n w_i, \quad i = 1, \ldots, L. \tag{5.7}$$

Using equation (5.7), we can then set $V(\bar{y}_{st})$ equal to $B^2/4$ and solve for n.

Similarly, estimation of the population total, τ, with a bound of B units on the error of estimation leads to the equation

$$2\sqrt{V(N\bar{y}_{st})} = B,$$

or, using equation (5.5),

$$V(\bar{y}_{st}) = \frac{B^2}{4N^2}.$$

The approximate sample size required to estimate μ or τ with a bound, B, on the error of estimation:

$$n = \frac{\displaystyle\sum_{i=1}^{L} \frac{N_i^2 \sigma_i^2}{w_i}}{N^2 D + \displaystyle\sum_{i=1}^{L} N_i \sigma_i^2}, \qquad (5.8)$$

where w_i is the fraction of observations allocated to stratum i and σ_i^2 is the population variance for stratum i.

$$D = \frac{B^2}{4} \quad \textit{when estimating } \mu.$$

$$D = \frac{B^2}{4N^2} \quad \textit{when estimating } \tau.$$

We must obtain approximations of the population variances $\sigma_1^2, \sigma_2^2, \ldots, \sigma_L^2$ before we can use formula (5.8). One method of obtaining these approximations is to use the sample variances $s_1^2, s_2^2, \ldots, s_L^2$ from a previous experiment to estimate $\sigma_1^2, \sigma_2^2, \ldots, \sigma_L^2$. A second method requires knowledge of the range of the observations within each stratum. From Tchebysheff's Theorem and the Empirical Rule it follows that the range should be roughly four to six standard deviations (see Section 2.2).

Methods of choosing the fractions $w_1, w_2, \ldots, w_L$ are given in Section 5.5.

Example 5.4

A prior survey suggests that the stratum variances in Example 5.1 are approximately $\sigma_1^2 \approx 25$, $\sigma_2^2 \approx 225$, and $\sigma_3^2 \approx 100$. We wish to estimate the population mean by using $\bar{y}_{st}$. Choose the sample size to obtain a bound on the error of estimation equal to two hours if the allocation fractions are given by $w_1 = 1/3$, $w_2 = 1/3$ and $w_3 = 1/3$. In other words you are to take an equal number of observations from each stratum.

Solution

A bound on the error of two hours means that

$$2\sqrt{V(\bar{y}_{st})} = 2$$

or

$$V(\bar{y}_{st}) = 1.$$

Therefore, $D = 1$.

In Example 5.1 $N_1 = 155$, $N_2 = 62$, and $N_3 = 93$. Therefore,

$$\sum_{i=1}^{3} \frac{N_i^2 \sigma_i^2}{w_i} = \frac{N_1^2 \sigma_1^2}{w_1} + \frac{N_2^2 \sigma_2^2}{w_2} + \frac{N_3^2 \sigma_3^2}{w_3}$$

$$= \frac{(155)^2(25)}{(1/3)} + \frac{(62)^2(225)}{(1/3)} + \frac{(93)^2(100)}{(1/3)}$$

$$= (24025)(75) + (3844)(675) + (8649)(300)$$

$$= 6{,}991{,}275,$$

$$\sum_{i=1}^{3} N_i \sigma_i^2 = N_1 \sigma_1^2 + N_2 \sigma_2^2 + N_3 \sigma_3^2$$

$$= (155)(25) + (62)(225) + (93)(100)$$

$$= 27{,}125$$

and

$$N^2 D = (310)^2(1) = 96{,}100.$$

From equation (5.8) we then have

$$n = \frac{\displaystyle\sum_{i=1}^{3} \frac{N_i^2 \sigma_i^2}{w_i}}{N^2 D + \displaystyle\sum_{i=1}^{3} N_i \sigma_i^2} = \frac{6{,}991{,}275}{96{,}100 + 27{,}125} = \frac{6{,}991{,}275}{123{,}225} = 56.7.$$

Thus, the experimenter should take $n = 57$ observations with

$$n_1 = n(w_1) = 57(1/3) = 19,$$

$$n_2 = 19,$$

and

$$n_3 = 19.$$

Example 5.5

As in Example 5.4, suppose the variances of Example 5.1 are approximated by $\sigma_1^2 \approx 25$, $\sigma_2^2 \approx 225$, and $\sigma_3^2 \approx 100$. We wish to estimate the population total, τ, with a bound of 400 hours on the error of estimation. Choose the appropriate sample size if an equal number of observations is to be taken from each stratum.

Solution

The bound on the error of estimation is to be 400 hours and, therefore,

$$D = \frac{B^2}{4N^2} = \frac{(400)^2}{4N^2} = \frac{40{,}000}{N^2}.$$

In order to calculate n from equation (5.8), we need the following quantities:

$$\sum_{i=1}^{3} \frac{N_i^2 \sigma_i^2}{w_i} = 6{,}991{,}275 \quad \text{(from Example 5.4)},$$

$$\sum_{i=1}^{3} N_i \sigma_i^2 = 27{,}125 \quad \text{(from Example 5.4)},$$

and

$$N^2 D = N^2 \left(\frac{40{,}000}{N^2} \right) = 40{,}000.$$

Using equation (5.8),

$$n = \frac{\displaystyle\sum_{i=1}^{3} \frac{N_i^2 \sigma_i^2}{w_i}}{N^2 D + \displaystyle\sum_{i=1}^{3} N_i \sigma_i^2}$$

$$= \frac{6{,}991{,}275}{40{,}000 + 27{,}125}$$

$$= 104.2, \text{ or } 105.$$

Then, $n_1 = n_2 = n_3 = 35.$

5.5   Allocation of the Sample

You recall that the objective of a sample survey design is to provide estimators with small variances at the lowest possible cost. After the sample size, n, is chosen, there are many ways to divide n into the individual stratum sample sizes, $n_1, n_2, \ldots, n_L$. Each division may result in a different variance for the sample mean. Hence our objective is to use an allocation which gives a specified amount of information at minimum cost.

In terms of our objective the best allocation scheme is affected by three factors. They are:

1. the total number of elements in each stratum,
2. the variability of observations within each stratum,
3. the cost of obtaining an observation from each stratum.

The number of elements in each stratum affects the quantity of information in the sample. A sample of size 20 from a population of 200 elements should contain more information than a sample of 20 from 20,000 elements. Thus, large sample sizes should be assigned to strata containing large numbers of elements.

Variability must be considered, because a larger sample is needed to obtain a good estimate of a population parameter when the observations are less homogeneous.

If the cost of obtaining an observation varies from stratum to stratum, we will take small samples from strata with high costs. We will do so because our objective is to keep the cost of sampling at a minimum.

The approximate allocation which minimizes cost for a fixed value of $V(\bar{y}_{st})$ or minimizes $V(\bar{y}_{st})$ for a fixed cost:

$$n_i = n \frac{N_i \sigma_i / \sqrt{c_i}}{N_1 \sigma_1 / \sqrt{c_1} + N_2 \sigma_2 / \sqrt{c_2} + \cdots + N_L \sigma_L / \sqrt{c_L}} \tag{5.9}$$

$$= n \frac{N_i \sigma_i / \sqrt{c_i}}{\sum_{i=1}^{L} N_i \sigma_i / \sqrt{c_i}},$$

where N_i denotes the size of the ith stratum, σ_i^2 denotes the population variance for the ith stratum, and c_i denotes the cost of obtaining a single observation from the ith stratum.

It is necessary to approximate the variance of each stratum before sampling in order to use the allocation formula (5.9). The approximations can be obtained from earlier surveys or from knowledge of the range of the measurements within each stratum.

Example 5.6

The advertising firm in Example 5.1 finds that it costs more to obtain an observation from a rural household than to obtain a response in town A or B. The increase is due to costs of traveling from one rural household to another. The cost per observation in each town is estimated to be \$9.00, (that is, $c_1 = c_2 = 9$), and the costs per observation in the rural area to be \$16.00, (that is, $c_3 = 16$). The stratum standard deviations (approximated by the strata sample variances from a prior survey) are $\sigma_1 \approx 5$, $\sigma_2 \approx 15$, and $\sigma_3 \approx 10$. Find the over-all sample size, n, and the stratum sample sizes, n_1, n_2, and n_3, which allow the firm to estimate, at minimum cost, the average television viewing time with a bound on the error of estimation equal to two hours.

Solution

Using equation (5.9) to find the proper allocation fractions we have

$$n_i = (n)\left[\frac{N_i\,\sigma_i/\sqrt{c_i}}{\sum\limits_{i=1}^{3} N_i\,\sigma_i/\sqrt{c_i}}\right],$$

where

$$\sum_{i=1}^{3}\frac{N_i\,\sigma_i}{\sqrt{c_i}} = \frac{N_1\sigma_1}{\sqrt{c_1}} + \frac{N_2\sigma_2}{\sqrt{c_2}} + \frac{N_3\sigma_3}{\sqrt{c_3}}$$

$$= \frac{155(5)}{\sqrt{9}} + \frac{62(15)}{\sqrt{9}} + \frac{93(10)}{\sqrt{16}}$$

$$= 800.83.$$

Then

$$n_1 = (n)\left[\frac{N_1\sigma_1/\sqrt{c_1}}{\sum\limits_{i=1}^{3} N_i\sigma_i/\sqrt{c_i}}\right] = (n)\left(\frac{155(5)/3}{800.83}\right) = .32\,n.$$

Similarly

$$n_2 = (n)\left(\frac{62(15)/3}{800.83}\right) = .39\,n,$$

and

$$n_3 = (n)\left(\frac{93(10)/4}{800.83}\right) = .29\,n.$$

From equation (5.7), $w_1 = .32$, $w_2 = .39$, and $w_3 = .29$.

We will now use equation (5.8) to find n. Since the bound on the error of estimation is two hours, it follows that

$$2\sqrt{V(\bar{y}_{st})} = 2,$$

or

$$V(\bar{y}_{st}) = 1.$$

Therefore, $D = B^2/4 = 1$ and $N^2 D = (310)^2 (1) = 96,100$. Also,

$$\sum_{i=1}^{3} \frac{N_i^2 \sigma_i^2}{w_i} = \frac{N_1^2 \sigma_1^2}{w_1} + \frac{N_2^2 \sigma_2^2}{w_2} + \frac{N_3^2 \sigma_3^2}{w_3}$$

$$= \frac{(155)^2 (5)^2}{.32} + \frac{(62)^2 (15)^2}{.39} + \frac{(93)^2 (10)^2}{.29}$$

$$= 7,077,059,$$

$$\sum_{i=1}^{3} N_i \sigma_i^2 = N_1 \sigma_1^2 + N_2 \sigma_2^2 + N_3 \sigma_3^2$$

$$= (155)(5)^2 + (62)(15)^2 + (93)(10)^2$$

$$= 27,125,$$

and from equation (5.8)

$$n = \frac{\displaystyle\sum_{i=1}^{3} \frac{N_i^2 \sigma_i^2}{w_i}}{N^2 D + \displaystyle\sum_{i=1}^{3} N_i \sigma_i^2} = \frac{7,077,059}{96,100 + 27,125}$$

$$= \frac{7,077,059}{123,225}$$

$$= 57.43, \text{ or } 58.$$

The corresponding allocation is given by

$$n_1 = nw_1 = 58(.32) = 18.5 \text{ or } 18,$$
$$n_2 = nw_2 = 58(.39) = 22.6 \text{ or } 23,$$

and

$$n_3 = nw_3 = 58(.29) = 16.8 \text{ or } 17.$$

Hence, the experimenter should select 18 households at random from town A, 23 from town B, and 17 from the rural area. He can then estimate the average number of hours spent watching television at minimum cost with a bound of two hours on the error of estimation.

In some stratified sampling problems the cost of obtaining an observation is the same for all strata. If the costs are unknown, we may be willing to assume that the costs per observation are equal. In this case the allocation formula (5.9) can still be used by letting $c_1 = c_2 = \cdots = c_L = 1$. When $c_1 = c_2 = \cdots = c_L$ and $w_1, w_2, \ldots, w_L$ are obtained by formula (5.9), the method of selecting the proportion of the sample size n to be assigned to each stratum is called *Neyman allocation*.

Neyman
Allae

Example 5.7

The advertising firm of Example 5.1 decides to use telephone interviews rather than personal interviews because all households in the county have telephones, and this method reduces costs. The cost of obtaining an observation is then the same in all three strata. The stratum standard deviations are again approximated by $\sigma_1 \approx 5$, $\sigma_2 \approx 15$, and $\sigma_3 \approx 10$. The firm desires to estimate the population mean, μ, with a bound on the error of estimation equal to two hours. Find the appropriate sample size, n, and stratum sample sizes, n_1, n_2, and n_3.

Solution

The costs are the same in all strata. Therefore, to find the allocation fractions, w_1, w_2, and w_3, we replace the costs by 1 in formula (5.9). Then,

$$\sum_{i=1}^{3} N_i \sigma_i = N_1 \sigma_1 + N_2 \sigma_2 + N_3 \sigma_3$$

$$= (155)(5) + (62)(15) + (93)(10)$$

$$= 2635,$$

and from (5.9)

$$n_1 = n \frac{N_1 \sigma_1}{\sum_{i=1}^{3} N_i \sigma_i} = n\left[\frac{(155)(5)}{2635}\right] = n(.30).$$

Similarly,

$$n_2 = n\left[\frac{(62)(15)}{2635}\right] = n(.35)$$

and

$$n_3 = n\left[\frac{(93)(10)}{2635}\right] = n(.35).$$

Thus, $w_1 = .30$, $w_2 = .35$, and $w_3 = .35$.

Now let us use equation (5.8) to find n. A bound of 2 hours on the error of estimation means that

$$2\sqrt{V(\bar{y}_{st})} = 2,$$

or

$$V(\bar{y}_{st}) = 1.$$

Therefore,

$$D = \frac{B^2}{4} = 1 \quad \text{and} \quad N^2 D + (310)^2(1) = 96{,}100.$$

Also,

$$\sum_{i=1}^{3} \frac{N_i^2 \sigma_i^2}{w_i} = \frac{N_1^2 \sigma_1^2}{w_1} + \frac{N_2^2 \sigma_2^2}{w_2} + \frac{N_3^2 \sigma_3^2}{w_3}$$

$$= \frac{(155)^2(5)^2}{.30} + \frac{(62)^2(15)^2}{.35} + \frac{(93)^2(10)^2}{.35}$$

$$= 6{,}944{,}369,$$

$$\sum_{i=1}^{3} N_i \sigma_i^2 = 27{,}125 \text{ from Example 5.5,}$$

and, from (5.8),

$$n = \frac{\displaystyle\sum_{i=1}^{3} \frac{N_i^2 \sigma_i^2}{w_i}}{N^2 D + \displaystyle\sum_{i=1}^{3} N_i \sigma_i^2} = \frac{6{,}944{,}369}{96{,}100 + 27{,}125} = 56.35 \text{ or } 57.$$

Then,

$$n_1 = nw_1 = (57)(.30) = 17,$$
$$n_2 = nw_2 = (57)(.35) = 20,$$

and

$$n_3 = nw_3 = (57)(.35) = 20.$$

The sample size, n, in this last example is nearly the same as in Example 5.6, but the allocation has changed. More observations are taken from the rural area because these observations no longer have a higher cost.

Example 5.8

An experimenter wanted to estimate the average weight of 90 rats (50 male and 40 female), being fed a certain diet. The rats were separated by sex; hence, it seemed appropriate to use stratified random sampling with two strata. To approximate the variability within each stratum, the experimenter selected the smallest and largest rats in each stratum and weighed them. He found that the range was 10 grams for the males and 8 grams for the females. How large a sample should have been taken in order to estimate the population average with a bound of 1 gram on the error of estimation? Assume cost of sampling was the same for both strata.

Solution

Let us denote males as stratum 1 and females as stratum 2. To use equation (5.9) we must first approximate σ_1 and σ_2. The standard deviation should be about one fourth of the range, assuming that the weights have a mound-shaped distribution. Thus,

$$\sigma_1 \approx \frac{10}{4} = 2.5 \text{ and } \sigma_2 \approx \frac{8}{4} = 2.0$$

From (5.9), with $c_1 = c_2 = 1$,

$$n_i = (n) \left[\frac{N_i \sigma_i}{\sum\limits_{i=1}^{2} N_i \sigma_i} \right],$$

where

$$\sum\limits_{i=1}^{2} N_i \sigma_i = (50)(2.5) + (40)(2.0) = 125 + 80 = 205.$$

Then

$$n_1 = (n) \left[\frac{N_1 \sigma_1}{\sum\limits_{i=1}^{2} N_i \sigma_i} \right] = (n) \left(\frac{125}{205} \right) = .61n$$

and

$$n_2 = n \left(\frac{80}{205} \right) = .39n.$$

Thus, $w_1 = .61$ and $w_2 = .39$.

We must calculate the following quantities in order to find n:

$$\sum_{i=1}^{2} \frac{N_i^2 \sigma_i^2}{w_i} = \frac{(50)^2(2.5)^2}{.61} + \frac{(40)^2(2.0)^2}{.39} = 42,025.01,$$

$$\sum_{i=1}^{2} N_i \sigma_i^2 = (50)(2.5)^2 + (40)(2.0)^2 = 472.50,$$

and

$$D = \frac{B^2}{4} = \frac{(1)^2}{4} = .25.$$

Using equation (5.8)

$$n = \frac{\displaystyle\sum_{i=1}^{2} \frac{N_i^2 \sigma_i^2}{w_i}}{N^2 D + \displaystyle\sum_{i=1}^{2} N_i \sigma_i^2} = \frac{42,025.01}{(90)^2(.25) + 472.50} = 16.83.$$

The sample size, n, should have been 17 with

$$n_1 = nw_1 = (17)(.61) = 10$$

and

$$n_2 = nw_2 = (17)(.39) = 7.$$

Just as we sometimes encounter equal costs per observation in all strata, we sometimes encounter approximately equal variances, $\sigma_1^2, \sigma_2^2, \ldots, \sigma_L^2$. If the variances are equal in all strata, then each of the variances $\sigma_1^2, \sigma_2^2, \ldots, \sigma_L^2$ can be replaced by 1 in formula (5.9) to simplify the calculation of the allocation fractions.

If costs, $c_1, c_2, \ldots, c_L$, are also equal for all strata, both the costs and the variances can be replaced by 1 in formula (5.9), and

$$n_i = n \frac{N_i}{N}, \qquad i = 1, \ldots, L. \tag{5.10}$$

This method of assigning sample sizes to the strata is called *proportional* allocation because sample sizes, $n_1, n_2, \ldots, n_L$, are proportional to stratum sizes, $N_1, N_2, \ldots, N_L$. Proportional allocation is often used if the strata variances cannot be approximated before sampling.

Example 5.9

The advertising firm in Example 5.1 thinks that the approximate variances used in previous examples are in error and that the stratum variances are approximately equal. The common value of σ_i was approximated by 10 in a preliminary study. Telephone interviews are to be used and hence costs will be equal in all strata. It is desired to estimate the average number of hours per week that households in the county watch television with a bound on the error of estimation equal to two hours. Find the sample size and stratum sample sizes necessary to achieve this accuracy.

Solution

The allocation fractions, w_i, are found by using formula (5.9) after replacing $\sigma_1, \ldots, \sigma_L$ and $c_1, \ldots, c_L$ by 1. Hence,

$$n_1 = n \frac{N_1}{\sum_{i=1}^{3} N_i} = n \frac{N_1}{N} = n\left(\frac{155}{310}\right) = n(.5),$$

$$n_2 = n \frac{N_2}{N} = n\left(\frac{62}{310}\right) = n(.2),$$

and

$$n_3 = n \frac{N_3}{N} = n\left(\frac{93}{310}\right) = n(.3),$$

Thus, $w_1 = .5$, $w_2 = .2$, and $w_3 = .3$.
  As in previous examples,

$$2\sqrt{V(\bar{y}_{st})} = 2,$$

or

$$V(\bar{y}_{st}) = 1.$$

Then $D = 1$ and $N^2 D = (310)^2(1) = 96{,}100$.
Also, since $\sigma_1 = \sigma_2 = \sigma_3 = 10$,

$$\sum_{i=1}^{3} \frac{N_i^2 \sigma_i^2}{w_i} = \frac{N_1^2 \sigma_1^2}{w_1} + \frac{N_2^2 \sigma_2^2}{w_2} + \frac{N_3^2 \sigma_3^2}{w_3}$$

$$= \frac{(155)^2(10)^2}{.5} + \frac{(62)^2(10)^2}{.2} + \frac{(93)^2(10)^2}{.3}$$

$$= 9{,}610{,}000.$$

and

$$\sum_{i=1}^{3} N_i\, \sigma_i^2 = N_1\sigma_1^2 + N_2\,\sigma_2^2 + N_3\,\sigma_3^2$$

$$= (155)(100) + (62)(100) + (93)(100)$$

$$= 310(100) = 31{,}000.$$

Then, from formula (5.8),

$$n = \frac{\displaystyle\sum_{i=1}^{3} \frac{N_i^2\sigma_i^2}{w_i}}{N^2 D + \displaystyle\sum_{i=1}^{3} N_i\,\sigma_i^2} = \frac{9{,}610{,}000}{96{,}100 + 31{,}000} = 75.6 \text{ or } 76.$$

It follows that

$$n_1 = nw_1 = (76)(.5) = 38,$$
$$n_2 = nw_2 = (76)(.2) = 15,$$

and

$$n_3 = nw_3 = (76)(.3) = 23.$$

These results differ from those of Example 5.7 because here the variances
are assumed to be equal in all strata and are approximated by a common
value.

The amount of money to be spent on sampling is sometimes fixed before the
experiment is started. Then the experimenter must find a sample size and allocation scheme which minimizes the variance of the estimator for a fixed
expenditure.

Example 5.10

In the television viewing example, suppose the costs are as specified in
Example 5.6. That is, $c_1 = c_2 = 9$ and $c_3 = 16$. Let the strata variances
be approximated by $\sigma_1 \approx 5$, $\sigma_2 \approx 15$, and $\sigma_3 \approx 10$. Given that the advertising firm has only \$500 to spend on sampling, choose the sample size
and allocation which minimize $V(\bar{y}_{st})$.

Solution

The allocation scheme is still given by formula (5.9.) In Example 5.6 we
found $w_1 = .32$, $w_2 = .39$, and $w_3 = .29$.

Since the total cost must equal \$500, we have

$$c_1 n_1 + c_2 n_2 + c_3 n_3 = 500,$$

or

$$9n_1 + 9n_2 + 16n_3 = 500.$$

Since $n_i = n w_i$, we can substitute as follows:

$$9nw_1 + 9nw_2 + 16nw_3 = 500,$$

or

$$9n(.32) + 9n(.30) + 16n(.29) = 500.$$

Solving for n we obtain

$$11.03n = 500,$$

or

$$n = \frac{500}{11.03} = 45.33.$$

Therefore, we must take $n = 45$ to insure that the cost remains below \$500. The corresponding allocation is given by

$$n_1 = nw_1 = (45)(.32) = 14,$$
$$n_2 = nw_2 = (45)(.39) = 18,$$

and

$$n_3 = nw_3 = (45)(.29) = 13.$$

5.6 Estimation of a Population Proportion

In our numerical examples we have been interested in estimating the average or the total number of hours per week spent watching television. In contrast, suppose that the advertising firm wants to estimate the proportion (fraction) of households that watches a particular show. The population is divided into strata, just as before, and a simple random sample is taken from each stratum. Interviews are then conducted to determine the proportion, $\hat{p}_i$, of households in stratum i that view the show. This $\hat{p}_i$ is an unbiased estimator of p_i, the population proportion in stratum i (as described in Chapter 4). Reasoning as we did in Section 5.3, we conclude that $N_i \hat{p}_i$ is an unbiased estimator of the total number of households in stratum i which view this particular show. Hence, $N_1 \hat{p}_1 + N_2 \hat{p}_2 + \cdots + N_L \hat{p}_L$ is a good estimator of the total number of households in the population. Dividing this quantity by N, we obtain an unbiased estimator of the population proportion, p, of households viewing the show.

Estimator of the population proportion p:

$$\hat{p}_{st} = \frac{1}{N} [N_1 \hat{p}_1 + N_2 \hat{p}_2 + \cdots + N_L \hat{p}_L] = \frac{1}{N} \sum_{i=1}^{L} N_i \hat{p}_i. \qquad (5.11)$$

Estimated variance of $\hat{p}_{st}$:

$$\hat{V}(\hat{p}_{st}) = \frac{1}{N^2} [N_1^2 \hat{V}(\hat{p}_1) + N_2^2 \hat{V}(\hat{p}_2) + \cdots + N_L^2 \hat{V}(\hat{p}_L)]$$

$$= \frac{1}{N^2} \sum_{i=1}^{L} N_i^2 \hat{V}(\hat{p}_i)$$

$$= \frac{1}{N^2} \sum_{i=1}^{L} N_i^2 \left(\frac{N_i - n_i}{N_i} \right) \frac{\hat{p}_i \hat{q}_i}{n_i - 1} . \qquad (5.12)$$

Bound on the error of estimation:

$$2 \sqrt{\hat{V}(\hat{p}_{st})} = 2 \sqrt{\frac{1}{N^2} \sum_{i=1}^{L} N_i^2 \left(\frac{N_i - n_i}{N_i} \right) \frac{\hat{p}_i \hat{q}_i}{n_i - 1}}. \qquad (5.13)$$

Example 5.11

The advertising firm wanted to estimate the proportion of households in the county of Example 5.1 that view show X. The county is divided into three strata, town A, town B, and the rural area. The strata contain $N_1 = 155$, $N_2 = 62$, and $N_3 = 93$ households, respectively. A stratified random sample of $n = 40$ households is chosen with proportional allocation. In other words, a simple random sample is taken from each stratum; the sizes of the samples are $n_1 = 20$, $n_2 = 8$, and $n_3 = 12$. Interviews are conducted in the 40 sampled households; results are shown in Table 5.3.

Table 5.3

Stratum	Sample size	Number of households viewing show X	$\hat{p}_i$
1	$n_1 = 20$	16	.80
2	$n_2 = 8$	2	.25
3	$n_3 = 12$	6	.50

Estimate the proportion of households viewing show X and place a bound on the error of estimation.

Solution

The estimate of the proportion of households viewing show X is given by $\hat{p}_{st}$. Using equation (5.11), we calculate

$$\hat{p}_{st} = \frac{1}{310} [(155)(.80) + 62(.25) + 93(.50)] = .60.$$

The variance of $\hat{p}_{st}$ can be estimated by using (5.12). First, let us calculate the $\hat{V}(\hat{p}_i)$ terms. We have

$$\hat{V}(\hat{p}_1) = \left(\frac{N_1 - n_1}{N_1}\right) \frac{\hat{p}_1 \hat{q}_1}{n_1 - 1} = \left(\frac{155 - 20}{155}\right) \frac{(.8)(.2)}{19} = (.871)(.008) = .007,$$

$$\hat{V}(\hat{p}_2) = \left(\frac{N_2 - n_2}{N_2}\right) \frac{\hat{p}_2 \hat{q}_2}{n_2 - 1} = \left(\frac{62 - 8}{62}\right) \frac{(.25)(.75)}{7} = (.871)(.027) = .024,$$

and

$$\hat{V}(\hat{p}_3) = \left(\frac{N_3 - n_3}{N_3}\right) \frac{\hat{p}_3 \hat{q}_3}{n_3 - 1} \left(\frac{93 - 12}{93}\right) \frac{(.5)(.5)}{11} = (.871)(.023) = .020.$$

From (5.12),

$$\hat{V}(\hat{p}_{st}) = \frac{1}{N^2} \sum_{i=1}^{3} N_i^2 \hat{V}(\hat{p}_i)$$

$$= \frac{1}{(310)^2} [(155)^2(.007) + (62)^2(.024) + (93)^2(.020)]$$

$$= .0045.$$

Then the estimate of proportion of households in the county which view show X with a bound on the error of estimation is given by

$$\hat{p}_{st} \pm 2\sqrt{\hat{V}(\hat{p}_{st})},$$

$$.60 \pm 2\sqrt{.0045},$$

$$.60 \pm 2(.0671),$$

or

$$.60 \pm .1342.$$

The bound on the error in Example 5.9 is quite large. We could reduce this bound and make the estimator more precise by increasing the sample size. The problem of choosing a sample size is considered in the following section.

5.7   Selecting the Sample Size and Allocating the Sample to Estimate Proportions

To estimate a population proportion we first indicate how much information we desire by specifying the size of the bound; the sample size is chosen accordingly.

The formula for the sample size n (for a given bound, B, on the error of estimation) is the same as equation (5.8) except that σ_i^2 becomes $p_i q_i$.

The approximate sample size required to estimate p with a bound, B, on the error of estimation:

$$n = \frac{\displaystyle\sum_{i=1}^{L} \frac{N_i^2 p_i q_i}{w_i}}{N^2 D + \displaystyle\sum_{i=1}^{L} N_i p_i q_i}, \qquad (5.14)$$

where w_i is the fraction of observations allocated to stratum i, p_i is the population proportion for stratum i, and

$$D = \frac{B^2}{4}.$$

The allocation formula which gives the variance of $\hat{p}_{st}$ equal to some fixed constant at minimum cost is the same as formula (5.9) with σ_i replaced by $\sqrt{p_i q_i}$.

The approximate allocation which minimizes cost for a fixed value of $V(\hat{p}_{st})$ or minimizes $V(p_{st})$ for a fixed cost:

$$n_i = n \frac{N_i\sqrt{p_i q_i/c_i}}{N_1\sqrt{p_1 q_1/c_1} + N_2\sqrt{p_2 q_2/c_2} + \cdots + N_L\sqrt{p_L q_L/c_L}}$$

$$= n \frac{N_i\sqrt{p_i q_i/c_i}}{\sum\limits_{i=1}^{L} N_i\sqrt{p_i q_i/c_i}}, \qquad (5.15)$$

where N_i denotes the size of the ith stratum, p_i denotes the population proportion for the ith stratum, and c_i denotes the cost of obtaining a single observation from the ith stratum.

Example 5.12

The data of Table 5.2 was obtained from a sample conducted last year. The advertising firm now wants to conduct a new survey in the same county to estimate the proportion of households viewing show X. Although the fractions p_1, p_2, and p_3 that appear in equations (5.14) and (5.15) are unknown, they can be approximated by the estimates from the earlier study, i.e., $\hat{p}_1 = .80$, $\hat{p}_2 = .25$, and $\hat{p}_3 = .50$. The cost of obtaining an observation is \$9 for either town and \$16 for the rural area, i.e., $c_1 = c_2 = 9$, and $c_3 = 16$. The number of households within the strata are $N_1 = 155$, $N_2 = 62$, and $N_3 = 93$. The firm wants to estimate the population proportion, p, with a bound on the error of estimation equal to .1. Find the sample size, n, and the strata sample sizes, n_1, n_2, and n_3, which will give the desired bound at minimum cost.

Solution

We first use (5.15) to find the allocation fractions, w_i. Using $\hat{p}_i$ to approximate p_i,

$$\sum_{i=1}^{3} N_i\sqrt{\hat{p}_i\hat{q}_i/c_i} = N_1\sqrt{\hat{p}_1\hat{q}_1/c_1} + N_2\sqrt{\hat{p}_2\hat{q}_2/c_2} + N_3\sqrt{\hat{p}_3\hat{q}_3/c_3}$$

$$= (155)\sqrt{(.8)(.2)/9} + 62\sqrt{(.25)(.75)/9} + 93\sqrt{(.5)(.5)/16}$$

$$= \frac{62.000}{3} + \frac{26.846}{3} + \frac{46.500}{4}$$

$$= 20.667 + 8.949 + 11.625$$

$$= 41.241,$$

and

$$n_1 = n \frac{N_1\sqrt{\hat{p}_1\hat{q}_1/c_1}}{\sum\limits_{i=1}^{3} N_i\sqrt{\hat{p}_i\hat{q}_i/c_i}} = n\left(\frac{20.667}{41.241}\right) = n(.50).$$

Similarly,

$$n_2 = n\left(\frac{8.949}{41.241}\right) = n(.22),$$

and

$$n_3 = n\left(\frac{11.625}{41.241}\right) = n(.28).$$

Thus, $w_1 = .50$, $w_2 = .22$, and $w_3 = .28$.

The next step is to use equation (5.14) to find n. First, the following quantities must be calculated:

$$\sum_{i=1}^{3} \frac{N_i^2 \hat{p}_i \hat{q}_i}{w_i} = \frac{N_1^2 \hat{p}_1 \hat{q}_1}{w_1} + \frac{N_2^2 \hat{p}_2 \hat{q}_2}{w_2} + \frac{N_3^2 \hat{p}_3 \hat{q}_3}{w_3}$$

$$= \frac{(155)^2(.8)(.2)}{.50} + \frac{(62)^2(.25)(.75)}{.22} + \frac{(93)^2(.5)(.5)}{.28}$$

$$= 18{,}686.46,$$

and

$$\sum_{i=1}^{3} N_i \hat{p}_i \hat{q}_i = N_1 \hat{p}_1 \hat{q}_1 + N_2 \hat{p}_2 \hat{q}_2 + N_3 \hat{p}_3 \hat{q}_3$$

$$= (155)(.8)(.2) + (62)(.25)(.75) + (93)(.5)(.5)$$

$$= 59.675.$$

To find D, we let $2\sqrt{V(\hat{p}_{st})} = .1$ (the bound on the error of estimation). Then,

$$V(\hat{p}_{st}) = \frac{(.1)^2}{4} = .0025 = D,$$

and

$$N^2 D = (310)^2(.0025) = 240.25.$$

Finally from (5.14), n is given approximately by

$$n = \frac{\displaystyle\sum_{i=1}^{3} \frac{N_i^2 \hat{p}_i \hat{q}_i}{w_i}}{N^2 D + \displaystyle\sum_{i=1}^{3} N_i \hat{p}_i \hat{q}_i} = \frac{18{,}686.46}{240.25 + 59.675} = 62.3 \text{ or } 63.$$

Hence,

$$n_1 = nw_1 = (63)(.50) = 31,$$
$$n_2 = nw_2 = (63)(.22) = 14,$$

and

$$n_3 = nw_3 = (63)(.28) = 18.$$

If the cost of sampling does not vary from stratum to stratum, then the cost factors, c_i, can be replaced by 1 in formula (5.15).

Example 5.13

Suppose that in Example 5.12 telephone interviews are to be conducted, and, hence, the cost of sampling is the same in all strata. The fraction p_i will be approximated by $\hat{p}_i$, $i = 1, 2, 3$. We desire to estimate the population proportion, p, with a bound of .1 on the error of estimation. Find the appropriate sample size to achieve this bound at minimum cost.

Solution

Equation (5.14) is used to find the fractions w_1, w_2, and w_3, but now all c_i terms can be replaced by 1. Hence,

$$\sum_{i=1}^{3} N_i \sqrt{\hat{p}_i \hat{q}_i} = 155\sqrt{(.8)(.2)} + 62\sqrt{(.25)(.75)} + 93\sqrt{(.5)(.5)}$$

$$= 62.000 + 26.846 + 46.500$$

$$= 135.346,$$

and

$$n_1 = n \frac{N_1 \sqrt{\hat{p}_1 \hat{q}_1}}{\sum_{i=1}^{3} N_i \sqrt{\hat{p}_i \hat{q}_i}} = n\left(\frac{62.000}{135.346}\right) = n(.46).$$

Similarly,

$$n_2 = n\left(\frac{26.846}{135.346}\right) = n(.20),$$

and

$$n_3 = n\left(\frac{46.500}{135.346}\right) = n(.34).$$

Thus, $w_1 = .46$, $w_2 = .20$, and $w_3 = .34$.

Equation (5.15) is now used to solve for n. We must first calculate

$$\sum_{i=1}^{3} \frac{N_i^2 \hat{p}_i \hat{q}_i}{w_i} = \frac{(155)^2(.8)(.2)}{.46} + \frac{(62)^2(.25)(.75)}{.20} + \frac{(93)^2(.5)(.5)}{.34}$$

$$= 18,319.83,$$

$$\sum_{i=1}^{3} N_i \hat{p}_i \hat{q}_i = 59.675 \text{ (from Example 5.12)},$$

and

$$N^2 D = 240.25 \text{ (from Example 5.12)}.$$

From (5.15), n is approximately

$$n = \frac{\displaystyle\sum_{i=1}^{3} \frac{N_i^2 \hat{p}_i \hat{q}_i}{w_i}}{N^2 D + \displaystyle\sum_{i=1}^{3} N_i \hat{p}_i \hat{q}_i} = \frac{18,319.83}{240.25 + 59.675} = 61.08 \text{ or } 62.$$

Hence, we take a sample of 62 observations to estimate p with a bound on the error of magnitude $B = .1$. The corresponding allocation is given by:

$$n_1 = n w_1 = 62(.46) = 29,$$
$$n_2 = n w_2 = 62(.20) = 12,$$

and

$$n_3 = n w_3 = 62(.34) = 21.$$

These answers are close to those of Example 5.12. The changes in allocation are due to the fact that costs do not vary in this example.

Recall that the allocation formula (5.9) assumes a very simple form when the variances, as well as costs, are equal for all strata. Equation (5.15) simplifies in the same way provided all stratum proportions, p_i, are equal and all costs, c_i, are equal. Then (5.15) becomes

$$n_i = n\,\frac{N_i}{N}, \qquad i = 1, \ldots, L.$$

As previously noted, this method for assignment of sample sizes to the strata is called *proportional* allocation.

Example 5.14

In the television survey Example 5.12, the advertising firm plans to use telephone interviews; therefore the cost of sampling will not vary from stratum to stratum. The stratum sizes are $N_1 = 155$, $N_2 = 62$, and $N_3 = 93$. The results of last year's survey (see Table 5.3) do not appear to hold for this year. The firm believes that the proportion of households viewing show X is close to .4 in each of the three strata. It is desired to estimate the population proportion, p, with a bound of .1 on the error of estimation. Find the sample size, n, and the allocation which gives this bound at minimum cost.

Solution

The allocation fractions are found by using equation (5.15) with $p_1, \ldots, p_L$ $c_1, \ldots, c_L$ replaced by 1. Thus

$$n_1 = n\,\frac{N_1}{\sum\limits_{i=1}^{3} N_i} = n\,\frac{N_1}{N} = n\left(\frac{155}{310}\right) = n(.5),$$

$$n_2 = n\,\frac{N_2}{N} = n\left(\frac{62}{310}\right) = n(.2),$$

and

$$n_3 = n\,\frac{N_3}{N} = n\left(\frac{93}{310}\right) = n(.3),$$

or

$$w_1 = .5, \quad w_2 = .2, \quad \text{and} \quad w_3 = .3.$$

The sample size n is found from equation (5.14), using .4 as an approximation to p_1, p_2, and p_3. It follows that

$$\sum_{i=1}^{3} \frac{N_i^2 p_i q_i}{w_i} = \frac{(155)^2(.4)(.6)}{.5} + \frac{(62)^2(.4)(.6)}{.2} + \frac{(93)^2(.4)(.4)}{.3}$$

$$= 23{,}064,$$

and

$$\sum_{i=1}^{3} N_i p_i q_i = (155)(.4)(.6) + (62)(.4)(.6) + (93)(.4)(.6)$$

$$= (.4)(.6)(155 + 62 + 93)$$

$$= (.4)(.6)(310)$$

$$= 74.4.$$

A bound of .1 on the error of estimation gives

$$2\sqrt{V(\hat{p}_{st})} = .1$$

or

$$V(\hat{p}_{st}) = (.05)^2 = .0025.$$

Hence, $D = .0025$ and

$$N^2 D = (310)^2(.0025) = 240.25.$$

From (5.14)

$$n = \frac{\sum_{i=1}^{3} \dfrac{N_i^2 p_i q_i}{w_i}}{N^2 D + \sum_{i=1}^{3} N_i p_i q_i} = \frac{23{,}064}{240.25 + 74.4} = 73.3 \text{ or } 74.$$

Then

$$n_1 = nw_1 = (74)(.5) = 37,$$

$$n_2 = nw_2 = (74)(.2) = 15,$$

and

$$n_3 = nw_3 = (74)(.3) = 22.$$

5.8   Additional Comments on Stratified Sampling

Stratified random sampling does not always produce an estimator with a smaller variance than that of the corresponding estimator in simple random sampling. The following example illustrates this point.

Example 5.15

A wholesale food distributor in a large city wants to know if demand is great enough to justify adding a new product to his stock. To aid in making his decision, he plans to add this product to a sample of the stores he services in order to estimate average monthly sales. He only services four large chains in the city. Hence, for administrative convenience, he decides to use stratified random sampling with each chain as a stratum. There are 24 stores in stratum 1, 36 in stratum 2, 30 in stratum 3, and 30 in stratum 4; Thus, $N_1 = 24$, $N_2 = 36$, $N_3 = 30$, $N_4 = 30$, and $N = 120$. The distributor has enough time and money to obtain data on monthly sales in $n = 20$ stores. Because he has no prior information on the stratum variances, and because the cost of sampling is the same in each stratum, he decides to use proportional allocation, which gives

$$n_1 = n\left(\frac{N_1}{N}\right) = (20)\left(\frac{24}{120}\right) = 4.$$

Similarly

$$n_2 = (20)\left(\frac{36}{120}\right) = 6,$$

$$n_3 = (20)\left(\frac{30}{120}\right) = 5,$$

and

$$n_4 = 5.$$

The new product is introduced in four stores, chosen at random from chain 1, six stores from chain 2, and five stores each from chains 3 and 4. The sales figures after a month show the following results:

Stratum	1	2	3	4
	94	91	108	92
	90	99	96	110
	102	93	100	94
	110	105	93	91
		111	93	113
		101		

$\bar{y}_1 = 99$, $\bar{y}_2 = 100$, $\bar{y}_3 = 98$, $\bar{y}_4 = 100$;
$s_1^2 = 78.67$, $s_2^2 = 55.60$, $s_3^2 = 39.50$, $s_4^2 = 112.50$.

Estimate the average sales for the month, and place a bound on the error of estimation.

Solution

From equation (5.1)

$$\bar{y}_{st} = \frac{1}{N} \sum_{i=1}^{4} N_i \bar{y}_i = 99.3.$$

Note that the estimate, $\bar{y}_{st}$, of the population mean is the average of all sample observations when proportional allocation is used.
    The estimated variance of $\bar{y}_{st}$, from equation (5.2), is

$$\hat{V}(\bar{y}_{st}) = \frac{1}{N^2} \sum_{i=1}^{4} N_i^2 \left(\frac{N_i - n_i}{N_i} \right) \frac{s_i^2}{n_i},$$

where for this example

$$\left(\frac{N_i - n_i}{N_i} \right) = \frac{5}{6}, \quad i = 1, 2, 3.$$

Then

$$\hat{V}(\bar{y}_{st}) = \frac{1}{(120)^2} \left(\frac{5}{6} \right) \left[(24)^2 \left(\frac{78.67}{4} \right) + (36)^2 \left(\frac{55.60}{6} \right) \right.$$

$$\left. + (30)^2 \left(\frac{39.50}{5} \right) + (30)^2 \left(\frac{112.50}{5} \right) \right]$$

$$= 2.9339,$$

and the estimate of average monthly sales with a bound on the error of estimation is

$$\bar{y}_{st} \pm 2\sqrt{\hat{V}(\bar{y}_{st})},$$

$$99.3 \pm 2\sqrt{2.9339},$$

or

$$99.3 \pm 3.4257.$$

Suppose the distributor had decided to take a simple random sample of $n = 20$ stores and the same 20 stores as above were selected. In other words, suppose the 20 stores constitute a simple random sample rather than a stratified random sample. Then the estimator of the population mean has the same value as that calculated above, that is,

$$\bar{y} = \bar{y}_{st} = 99.3,$$

but the estimated variance becomes

$$\hat{V}(\bar{y}) = \left(\frac{N-n}{N}\right)\frac{s^2}{n} = \left(\frac{5}{6}\right)\frac{59.8}{20} = 2.492.$$

We see that the estimated variance is *smaller* for simple random sampling. Thus we conclude simple random sampling may have been better than stratified random sampling for this problem. The experimenter did not consider the fact that sales vary greatly among stores within a chain when he stratified on chains. He could have obtained a smaller variance for his estimator by stratifying on amount of sales, that is, by putting stores with low monthly sales in one stratum, stores with high sales in another, and so forth.

In many sample survey problems more than one measurement is taken on each sampling unit in order to estimate more than one population parameter. This situation causes complications in selecting the appropriate sample size and allocation, as is illustrated in the following example.

Example 5.16

A state forest service is conducting a study of the people who use state-operated camping facilities. The state has two camping areas, one located in the mountains and one located along the coast. The forest service wishes to estimate the average number of people per campsite and the proportion of campsites occupied by out-of-state campers during a particular weekend when all sites are expected to be used. The average number of people is to be estimated with a bound of 1 on the error of estimation, and the proportion of out-of-state users is to be estimated with a bound of .1. The two camping areas conveniently form two strata, the mountain location forming stratum 1 and the coastal location stratum 2. It is known that $N_1 = 120$ campsites and $N_2 = 80$ campsites. Find the sample size and allocation necessary to achieve both of the above bounds.

Solution

Assuming that the costs of sampling are the same in each stratum, we could achieve the smallest sample size by using Neyman allocation. However, this allocation depends on the stratum variances and gives different allocations for the two different types of measurements involved in the problem. Instead, we use proportional allocation because it is usually close to optimum and it gives the same allocation for any desired measurement. It follows that

$$w_1 = \frac{N_1}{N} = \frac{120}{200} = .6$$

and

$$w_2 = \frac{N_2}{N} = \frac{80}{200} = .4.$$

Now, the sample size must be determined separately for each of the desired estimates. First consider estimating the average number of persons per campsite. It is necessary to have an approximation of the stratum variances in order to use equation (5.8) for the sample size. The forest service knows from experience that most sites contain from 1 to 9 persons. Therefore, we can use the approximation

$$\sigma_i \approx \frac{9-1}{4} = 2, \quad i = 1, 2.$$

It follows that

$$\sum_{i=1}^{2} \frac{N_i^2 \sigma_i^2}{w_i} = \frac{(120)^2(4)}{.6} + \frac{(80)^2(4)}{.4} = 160{,}000,$$

$$\sum_{i=1}^{2} N_i \sigma_i^2 = (120)(4) + (80)(4) = 800,$$

and

$$N^2 D = N^2 \left(\frac{B^2}{4} \right) = (200)^2 \left(\frac{1}{4} \right) = 10{,}000.$$

From equation (5.8),

$$n = \frac{\displaystyle\sum_{i=1}^{2} \frac{N_i^2 \sigma_i^2}{w_i}}{N^2 D + \displaystyle\sum_{i=1}^{2} N_i \sigma_i^2}$$

$$= \frac{160{,}000}{10{,}000 + 800} = 14.8, \text{ or } 15.$$

is the required sample size.

Now, let us consider estimating the proportion of out-of-state users. No prior estimates of the stratum proportions, p_i, are available, so we let $p_1 = p_2 = .5$ to obtain a maximum sample size. We use equation (5.14) to find n and, hence, we must find

$$\sum_{i=1}^{2} \frac{N_i^2 p_i q_i}{w_i} = \frac{(120)^2(.5)(.5)}{.6} + \frac{(80)^2(.5)(.5)}{.4}$$

$$= 10,000,$$

$$N^2 D = N^2 \left(\frac{B^2}{4} \right) = (200)^2 \left(\frac{.01}{4} \right) = 100.$$

$$\sum_{i=1}^{2} N_i p_i q_i = 120(.5)(.5) + 80(.5)(.5) = 50.$$

From equation (5.14),

$$n = \frac{\displaystyle\sum_{i=1}^{2} \frac{N_i^2 p_i q_i}{w_i}}{N^2 D + \displaystyle\sum_{i=1}^{2} N_i p_i q_i}$$

$$= \frac{10,000}{100 + 50} = 67.$$

Thus,

$$n_1 = n w_1 = (67)(.6) = 40$$

and

$$n_2 = n w_2 = (67)(.4) = 27$$

are the sample sizes required in order to achieve both bounds. Note that these sample sizes give an estimate of the average number of persons per campsite with a much smaller bound than required.

5.9 Summary

A stratified random sample is obtained by separating the population elements into groups, or strata, such that each element belongs to one and only one stratum, and then independently selecting a simple random sample from each stratum. This sample survey design has three major advantages over simple random sampling. First, the variance of the estimator of the population mean is usually reduced because the variance of observations within each stratum is usually smaller than the overall population variance. Second, the cost of collecting and analyzing the data is often reduced by the separation of a large population into smaller strata. Third, separate estimates can be obtained for individual strata without selecting another sample and, hence, without additional cost.

An unbiased estimator, $\bar{y}_{st}$, of the population mean is a weighted average of the sample means for the strata; it is given by (5.1). An unbiased estimator of the variance of $\bar{y}_{st}$ is given by (5.2); this estimator is used in placing bounds on the error of estimation. An unbiased estimator of the population total is also given, along with its estimated variance.

Before conducting a survey, an experimenter should consider how large an error of estimation he will tolerate and then should select the sample size accordingly. The sample size, n, is given by (5.8) for a fixed bound, B, on the error of estimation. The sample must then be allocated among the various strata. The allocation which gives a fixed amount of information at minimum cost is given by equation (5.9); it is affected by the stratum sizes, the stratum variances, and the costs of obtaining observations.

The estimator $\hat{p}_{st}$ of a population proportion has the same form as $\bar{y}_{st}$ and is given by (5.11). An unbiased estimator of $V(\hat{p}_{st})$ is given by (5.12). The related allocation and sample size problems have the same solutions as above, except that σ^2 is replaced by $p_i q_i$.

References

Cochran, W. G., *Sampling Techniques*, 2d ed., New York: John Wiley and Sons, Inc., 1963.

Hansen, M. H., W. N. Hurwitz, and W. G. Madow, *Sample Survey Methods and Theory*, Vol. 1, New York: John Wiley and Sons, Inc., 1953.

Kish, L., *Survey Sampling*, New York: John Wiley and Sons, Inc., 1965.

Exercises

5.1   A chain of department stores is interested in estimating the proportion of accounts receivable that are delinquent. The chain consists of four stores. To reduce the cost of sampling, stratified random sampling is used with each store as a stratum. Since no information on population proportions is available before sampling, proportional allocation is used. From the table given below, estimate p, the proportion of delinquent accounts for the chain, and place a bound on the error of estimation.

Stratum	I	II	III	IV
Number of accounts receivable	$N_1 = 65$	$N_2 = 42$	$N_3 = 93$	$N_4 = 25$
Sample size	$n_1 = 14$	$n_2 = 9$	$n_3 = 21$	$n_4 = 6$
Sample proportion of delinquent accounts	$\hat{p}_1 = .3$	$\hat{p}_2 = .2$	$\hat{p}_3 = .4$	$\hat{p}_4 = .1$

5.2 A corporation desires to estimate the total number of man-hours lost, for a given month, because of accidents among all employees. Since laborers, technicians, and administrators have different accident rates, it is decided to use stratified random sampling with each group forming a separate stratum. Data from previous years suggest the following variances for the number of man-hours lost per employee in the three groups and current data give the following stratum sizes:

I (Laborers)	II (Technicians)	III (Administrators)
$\sigma_1^2 = 36$	$\sigma_2^2 = 25$	$\sigma_3^2 = 9$
$N_1 = 132$	$N_2 = 92$	$N_3 = 27$

Determine the Neyman allocation for a sample of $n = 30$ employees.

5.3 For Exercise 5.2 estimate the total number of man-hours lost during the given month and place a bound on the error of estimation. Use the following data obtained from sampling 18 laborers, 10 technicians, and 2 administrators:

I (Laborers)			II (Technicians)		III (Administrators)
8	24	0	4	5	1
0	16	32	0	24	8
6	0	16	8	12	
7	4	4	3	2	
9	5	8	1	8	
18	2	0			

5.4 A zoning commission is formed to estimate the average appraised value of houses in a residential suburb of a city. It is convenient to use the two voting districts in the suburb as strata because separate lists of dwellings are available for each district. From the data given below, estimate the average appraised value for all houses in the suburb and place a bound on the error of estimation (note that proportional allocation was used):

Stratum I	Stratum II
$N_1 = 110$	$N_2 = 168$
$n_1 = 20$	$n_2 = 30$
$\sum_{i=1}^{n_1} y_i = 240{,}000$	$\sum_{i=1}^{n_2} y_i = 420{,}000$
$\sum_{i=1}^{n_1} y_i^2 = 2{,}980{,}000{,}000$	$\sum_{i=1}^{n_2} y^2 = 6{,}010{,}000{,}000$

5.5   A corporation wishes to obtain information on the effectiveness of a busi-
       ness machine. A number of division heads will be interviewed by telephone
       and asked to rate the equipment on a numerical scale. The divisions are
       located in North America, Europe, and Asia. Hence, stratified sampling
       is used. The costs are larger for interviewing division heads located outside
       of North America. The following costs per interview, approximate
       variances of the ratings, and N_i's have been established:

Stratum I (North America)   II (Europe)   III (Asia)

$c_1 = \$9$	$c_2 = \$25$	$c_3 = \$36$
$\sigma_1^2 = 2.25$	$\sigma_2^2 = 3.24$	$\sigma_3^2 = 3.24$
$N_1 = 112$	$N_2 = 68$	$N_3 = 39$

       The corporation wants to estimate the average rating with $V(\bar{y}_{st}) = .1$.
       Choose the sample size, n, which achieves this bound and find the
       appropriate allocation.

5.6   A school desires to estimate the average score that would be obtained on
       a reading comprehension exam for students in the sixth grade. The school
       has students divided into three tracks, with the fast learners in track I and
       the slow learners in track III. It was decided to stratify on tracks since this
       method should reduce variability of test scores. The sixth grade contains
       55 students in track I, 80 in track II, and 65 in track III. A stratified
       random sample of 50 students is proportionally allocated and yields simple
       random samples of $n_1 = 14$, $n_2 = 20$, and $n_3 = 16$ from tracks I, II, and III,
       respectively. The test is administered to the sample of students with the
       following results:

Track I		Track II		Track III	
80	92	85	82	42	32
68	85	48	75	36	31
72	87	53	73	65	29
85	91	65	78	43	19
90	81	49	69	53	14
62	79	72	81	61	31
61	83	53	59	42	30
		68	52	39	32
		71	61		
		59	42		

       Estimate the average score for the sixth grade, and place a bound on the
       error of estimation.

5.7   Suppose the average test score for the class in Exercise 5.6 is to be esti-
       mated again at the end of the school year. The costs of sampling are equal
       in all strata, but the variances differ. Find the optimum (Neyman) alloca-
       tion of a sample of size 50 using the data of Exercise 5.6 to approximate
       the variances.

5.8   Using the data of Exercise 5.6, find the sample size required to estimate the average score with a bound of 4 points on the error of estimation. Use proportional allocation.

5.9   Repeat Exercise 5.8 using Neyman allocation. Compare the result with the answer to Exercise 5.8.

5.10 A forester wants to estimate the total number of farm-acres planted in trees for a state. Since the number of acres of trees varies considerably with the size of the farm, it is decided to stratify on farm sizes. The 240 farms in the state are placed in one of four categories according to size. A stratified random sample of 40 farms, selected using proportional allocation, yields the following results on number of acres planted in trees.

Stratum I 0–200 Acres		Stratum II 200–400 Acres		Stratum III 400–600 Acres		Stratum IV Over 600 Acres	
$N_1 = 86$		$N_2 = 72$		$N_3 = 52$		$N_4 = 30$	
$n_1 = 14$		$n_2 = 12$		$n_3 = 9$		$n_4 = 5$	
97	67	125	155	142	256	167	655
42	125	67	96	310	440	220	540
25	92	256	47	495	510	780	
105	86	310	236	320	396		
27	43	220	352	196			
45	59	142	190				
53	21						

Estimate the total number of acres of trees on farms in the state, and place a bound on the error of estimation.

5.11 The study of Exercise 5.10 is to be made yearly with the bound on the error of estimation 500 acres. Find an approximate sample size to achieve this bound if Neyman allocation is to be used. Use the data in Exercise 5.10.

5.12 A psychologist working with a group of mentally retarded adults desires to estimate their average reaction time to a certain stimulus. He feels that men and women probably will show a difference in reaction times so he wants to stratify on sex. The group of 96 people contains 43 men. In previous studies of this type it has been observed that the times range from 5 to 20 seconds for men and from 3 to 14 seconds for women. The costs of sampling are the same for both strata. Using optimum allocation find the approximate sample size necessary to estimate the average reaction time for the group to within 1 second.

5.13 A county government is interested in expanding the facilities of a day-care center for mentally retarded children. The expansion would increase the cost of enrolling a child in the center. A sample survey will be conducted to estimate the proportion of families with retarded children that would make use of the expanded facilities. The families are divided into those who use the existing facilities and those who do not. Some families live in the city in which the center is located and some live in the surrounding suburban and rural areas. Thus, stratified random sampling is used with users in the city, users in the surrounding county, nonusers in the city, and nonusers in the county forming strata 1, 2, 3, and 4, respectively. Approximately 90% of the present users and 50% of the present nonusers would use the expanded facilities. The cost of obtaining an observation from a user is $4.00 and from a nonuser is $8.00. The difference in cost is due to the fact that nonusers are difficult to locate.

Existing records give $N_1 = 97$, $N_2 = 43$, $N_3 = 145$, and $N_4 = 68$. Find the approximate sample size and allocation necessary to estimate the population proportion with a bound of .05 on the error of estimation.

5.14   The survey of Exercise 5.13 was conducted and yields the following proportion of families who would use the new facilities:

$$\hat{p}_1 = .87, \quad \hat{p}_2 = .93, \quad \hat{p}_3 = .60, \quad \hat{p}_4 = .53.$$

Estimate the population proportion, p, and place a bound on the error of estimation. Was the desired bound achieved?

5.15   Suppose in Exercise 5.13 the total cost of sampling is fixed at $400. Choose the sample size and allocation which minimizes the variance of the estimator, $\hat{p}_{st}$, for this fixed cost.

6

Ratio Estimation

6.1   Introduction

Estimation of the population mean and total in preceding chapters was based on a sample of response measurements, $y_1, y_2, \ldots, y_n$, obtained by simple random sampling (Chapter 4) and stratified random sampling (Chapter 5). Sometimes other variables are closely related to the response, y. By measuring y and one or more subsidiary variables, we can obtain additional information for estimating the population mean. The reader should be familiar with the use of subsidiary variables to estimate the mean of a response, y. It is basic to the concept of correlation and provides means for development of a prediction equation relating y and x by the method of least squares. This topic is ordinarily covered in introductory courses in statistics (Mendenhall, 1971, Chapter 10).

Chapters 4 and 5 presented simple estimators of population parameters utilizing the response measurements $y_1, y_2, \ldots, y_n$; however, primary emphasis was placed on the design of the sample survey (simple and stratified random sampling). In contrast, Chapter 6 presents a new method of estimation based on the use of a subsidiary variable, x. This method is called *ratio estimation*. It requires the measurement of *two* variables, y and x, on each element of the sample, and it can be used with many types of sample survey designs. We will restrict our attention solely to ratio estimation for simple random sampling, because it is used most frequently in practice and because it demonstrates the general concept of ratio estimation.

6.2   Surveys That Require the Use of Ratio Estimators

Estimating a population total sometimes requires the use of subsidiary variables. We illustrate the use of a *ratio estimator* for one of these situations. The wholesale price paid for oranges in large shipments is based on the sugar content of the load. The exact sugar content cannot be determined prior to the purchase and extraction of the juice from the entire load; however, it can be estimated. One method of estimating this quantity is to first estimate the mean sugar content per orange, μ_y, and then to multiply by the number of oranges, N, in the load. Thus, we could randomly sample n oranges from the load to determine the sugar content, y, for each. The average of these sample measurements, $y_1, y_2, \ldots, y_n$, would estimate μ_y; $N\bar{y}$ would estimate the total sugar content for the load, τ_y. Unfortunately, this method is not feasible because it would be too time consuming and costly to determine N (that is, to count the total number of oranges in the load).

We can avoid the need to know N by noting the following two facts. First, the sugar content of an individual orange, y, is closely related to its weight, x; second, the ratio of the total sugar content, τ_y, to the total weight of the truck load, τ_x, is equal to the ratio of the mean sugar content per orange, μ_y, to the mean weight, μ_x. Thus,

$$\frac{\mu_y}{\mu_x} = \frac{N\mu_y}{N\mu_x} = \frac{\tau_y}{\tau_x}.$$

Solving for the total sugar content of the load, we have

$$\tau_y = \frac{\mu_y}{\mu_x}(\tau_x).$$

We can estimate μ_y and μ_x using $\bar{y}$ and $\bar{x}$, the averages of the sugar contents and weights for the sample of n oranges. Also, we can measure τ_x, the total weight of the oranges on the truck. Then a *ratio* estimator of the total sugar content, τ_y, is

$$\hat{\tau}_y = \frac{\bar{y}}{\bar{x}}(\tau_x)$$

or, equivalently, (multiplying numerator and denominator by n),

$$\hat{\tau}_y = \left(\frac{n\bar{y}}{n\bar{x}}\right)(\tau_x) = \frac{\sum\limits_{i=1}^{n} y_i}{\sum\limits_{i=1}^{n} x_i}\ (\tau_x).$$

In this case the number of elements in the population, N, is unknown, and therefore it is impossible to use the simple estimator, $N\bar{y}$, of the population total, τ_y (Section 4.3). Thus, a ratio estimator or its equivalent is necessary to accomplish the estimation objective. However, if N is known, we have the choice of using the estimator $N\bar{y}$ or the ratio estimator to estimate τ_y. If y and x are highly correlated, that is, x contributes information for the prediction of y, the ratio estimator should be better than $N\bar{y}$, which depends solely on $\bar{y}$.

In addition to the population total, τ_y, there are often other parameters of interest. We may want to estimate the population mean, μ_y, using a ratio estimation procedure. For example, suppose it is necessary to estimate the average sugar content per orange in a large shipment. We could use the sample mean $\bar{y}$ to estimate μ_y. However, if x and y are correlated, a ratio estimator that uses information from the auxiliary variable x frequently provides a more precise estimator of μ_y.

The population ratio is another parameter which could be of interest to an investigator. For example, assume we want to estimate the ratio of total automobile sales for the first quarter of this year to the number of sales during the corresponding period of the previous year. Let τ_x be the total number of sales for the first quarter of last year, and let τ_y be the total number of sales for the same period this year. We are interested in estimating the ratio

$$R = \frac{\tau_y}{\tau_x}.$$

In the following sections we will consider how to estimate μ_y, τ_y, and R using a ratio estimator. Whenever appropriate, comparisons will be made to the estimators of these parameters presented in previous chapters.

6.3   Ratio Estimation Using Simple Random Sampling

Let us assume that a simple random sample of size n is to be drawn from a finite population containing N elements. How then do we estimate a population mean, μ_y, a total, τ_y, or a ratio, R, utilizing sample information on y and a subsidiary variable, x?

Estimator of the population ratio R:

$$\hat{R} = r = \frac{\sum\limits_{i=1}^{n} y_i}{\sum\limits_{i=1}^{n} x_i}.$$

(6.1)

Estimated variance of r:

$$\hat{V}(r) = \hat{V}\left[\frac{\sum\limits_{i=1}^{n} y_i}{\sum\limits_{i=1}^{n} x_i}\right] = \left(\frac{N-n}{nN}\right)\left(\frac{1}{\mu_x^2}\right)\frac{\sum\limits_{i=1}^{n}(y_i - rx_i)^2}{n-1}.$$

(6.2)

Bound on the error of estimation:

$$2\sqrt{\hat{V}(r)} = 2\sqrt{\left(\frac{N-n}{nN}\right)\left(\frac{1}{\mu_x^2}\right)\frac{\sum\limits_{i=1}^{n}(y_i - rx_i)^2}{n-1}}.$$

(6.3)

(If the population mean for x, μ_x, is unknown, one would use $\bar{x}^2$ to approximate μ_x^2 in equations (6.2) and (6.3).)

Example 6.1

In a survey to examine trends in real estate, an investigator is interested in the relative change over a two year period in the assessed value of homes in a particular community. A simple random sample of $n = 20$ homes is selected from the $N = 1000$ homes in the community. From tax records, the investigator obtains the assessed value for this year (y) and the corresponding value for two years ago (x) for each of the $n = 20$ homes included in the sample. He wishes to estimate R, the relative change in assessed value for the $N = 100$ homes, using information contained in the sample.

The data for the real estate survey are presented in Table 6.1. We have added the x_i^2, y_i^2, and $x_i y_i$ columns, which are useful in the calculation of $\hat{V}(r)$.

Using the data in Table 6.1, estimate R, the relative change in real estate valuation over the given two year period. Place a bound on the error of estimation.

Table 6.1   Data and calculation for the real estate valuation survey

Home	Assessed value 2 years ago x_i	Current value y_i	x_i^2	y_i^2	$x_i y_i$
1	20.2	24.2	408.04	585.64	488.84
2	25.4	29.9	645.16	894.00	759.46
3	26.1	31.8	681.21	1011.24	829.98
4	29.5	36.0	870.25	1296.00	1062.00
5	24.3	28.7	590.49	823.69	697.41
6	22.1	26.0	488.41	676.00	574.60
7	23.7	28.9	561.69	835.21	684.93
8	24.9	30.3	620.01	918.09	754.47
9	21.5	25.2	462.25	635.04	541.80
10	28.2	33.3	795.24	1108.89	939.6
11	28.6	34.2	817.96	1169.64	978.12
12	26.9	32.0	723.61	1024.00	860.80
13	25.2	30.3	635.04	918.09	763.56
14	24.1	29.4	580.81	864.36	708.54
15	23.9	28.2	571.21	795.24	673.98
16	23.1	28.1	533.61	789.61	649.11
17	27.5	33.2	756.25	1102.24	913.00
18	30.2	35.6	912.04	1267.36	1075.12
19	31.4	38.6	924.16	1489.96	1212.04
20	29.3	34.3	858.49	1176.49	1004.99
	516.1	618.2	13,497.73	19,380.80	16,171.81

Solution

The estimate of R using the sample data is given by

$$r = \frac{\sum_{i=1}^{20} y_i}{\sum_{i=1}^{20} x_i} = \frac{\text{total current valuation of the 20 homes}}{\text{total valuation of the 20 homes 2 years ago}}.$$

Using Table 6.1,

$$r = \frac{618.2}{516.1} = 1.19783.$$

Hence, we estimate that real estate valuation has increased approximately 20% over a two year period in the area studied.

The bound on the error of estimation is found using equation (6.3). A shortcut method for calculating $\sum_{i=1}^{n} (y_i - rx_i)^2$, needed in $\hat{V}(r)$, is given by

$$\sum_{i=1}^{n} (y_i - rx_i)^2 = \sum_{i=1}^{n} y_i^2 + r^2 \sum_{i=1}^{n} x_i^2 - 2r \sum_{i=1}^{n} x_i y_i. \tag{6.4}$$

These quantities can be obtained from Table 6.1:

$$\sum_{i=1}^{20} (y_i - rx_i)^2 = 19380.80 + (1.19783)^2(13497.73)$$

$$- 2(1.19783)(16171.81)$$

$$= 5.14024.$$

Using equation (6.3),

$$2\sqrt{\hat{V}(r)} = 2\sqrt{\left(\frac{N-n}{nN}\right)\left(\frac{1}{\bar{x}^2}\right)\frac{\sum_{i=1}^{n}(y_i - rx_i)^2}{n-1}}$$

$$= 2\sqrt{\frac{1000-20}{20(1000)}\frac{1}{(25.805)^2}\left(\frac{5.14024}{19}\right)}$$

$$= .00892.$$

Thus, we estimate the ratio of real estate valuation to be $r = 1.198$, and we are quite confident that the error of estimation is less than .00892. You will note that the bound on the error of estimation is relatively small; hence, $r = 1.198$ should be a fairly accurate estimate of the population ratio, R.

The ratio technique for estimating a population total, τ_y, was applied in estimating the total sugar content of a truckload of oranges. The simple estimator, $\hat{\tau}_y = N\bar{y}$, is not applicable because we do not know N, the total number of oranges in the truck. The following ratio estimation procedure can be applied in estimating τ_y whether or not N is known.

Ratio estimator of the population total τ_y:

$$\hat{\tau}_y = \frac{\sum_{i=1}^{n} y_i}{\sum_{i=1}^{n} x_i}(\tau_x) = r\tau_x. \qquad (6.5)$$

Estimated variance of $\hat{\tau}_y$:

$$\hat{V}(\hat{\tau}_y) = (\tau_x)^2 \hat{V}(r) = (\tau_x^2)\left(\frac{N-n}{nN}\right)\left(\frac{1}{\mu_x^2}\right)\frac{\sum_{i=1}^{n}(y_i - rx_i)^2}{n-1}, \qquad (6.6)$$

where μ_x and τ_x are the population mean and total, respectively, for the random variable x.

Bound on the error of estimation:

$$2\sqrt{\hat{V}(\hat{\tau}_y)} = 2\sqrt{(\tau_x^2)\left(\frac{N-n}{nN}\right)\left(\frac{1}{\mu_x^2}\right)\frac{\sum\limits_{i=1}^{n}(y_i - rx_i)^2}{n-1}}.$$ (6.7)

You will note that although it is not necessary to know N or μ_x, we must know τ_x in order to estimate τ_y by use of the ratio estimation procedure.

Example 6.2

To estimate the total sugar content of a truck load of oranges, a random sample of $n = 10$ oranges was juiced and weighed (see Table 6.2). The total weight of all the oranges, obtained by first weighing the truck loaded and then unloaded, was found to be 1800 pounds. Estimate τ_y, the total sugar content for the oranges, and place a bound on the error of estimation.

Table 6.2

Orange	Sugar content (in lbs)	Weight of orange (in lbs)
1	.021	.40
2	.030	.48
3	.025	.43
4	.022	.42
5	.033	.50
6	.027	.46
7	.019	.39
8	.021	.41
9	.023	.42
10	.025	.44
	$\sum\limits_{i=1}^{10} y_i = .246$	$\sum\limits_{i=1}^{10} x_i = 4.35$

Solution

The sugar content of an orange is usually recorded in degrees brix, which is a measure of the number of pounds of solids (mostly sugar) per 100 pounds of juice. For our calculations, we shall use the actual pounds per orange. An estimate of τ_y can be obtained using equation (6.5).

$$\hat{\tau}_y = r\tau_x = \frac{\sum\limits_{i=1}^{10} y_i}{\sum\limits_{i=1}^{10} x_i}(\tau_x) = \frac{.246}{4.35}(1800) = 101.79 \text{ pounds.}$$

A bound on the error of estimation can be found if we use a modified version of equation (6.7). Because N is unknown in this example, we assume that the finite population correction, $(N - n)/N$, is near unity. This is reasonable because we expect at least $N = 4000$ oranges even in a small truck load. The sample mean $\bar{x}$ must be used in place of μ_x in equation (6.7), because μ_x is unknown. With these adjustments equation (6.7) becomes

$$2\sqrt{\hat{V}(\hat{\tau}_y)} = 2\sqrt{\tau_x^2 \left(\frac{1}{n}\right) \cdot \left(\frac{1}{\bar{x}^2}\right) \frac{\sum\limits_{i=1}^{n}(y_i - rx_i)^2}{n - 1}}.$$

Using equation (6.4), for computational ease,

$$\sum_{i=1}^{10}(y_i - rx_i)^2 = \sum_{i=1}^{10} y_i^2 + r^2 \sum_{i=1}^{10} x_i^2 - 2r \sum_{i=1}^{10} x_i y_i,$$

where

$$r = \frac{\sum\limits_{i=1}^{10} y_i}{\sum\limits_{i=1}^{10} x_i} = \frac{.246}{4.35} = .0566.$$

From the data,

$$\sum_{i=1}^{10} y_i^2 = (.021)^2 + (.030)^2 + \cdots + (.025)^2 = .006224,$$

$$\sum_{i=1}^{10} x_i^2 = (.40)^2 + (.48)^2 + \cdots + (.44)^2 = 1.9035,$$

$$\sum_{i=1}^{10} y_i x_i = (.021)(.40) + (.030)(.48) + \cdots + (.025)(.44) = .10839,$$

and

$$\bar{x} = \frac{4.35}{10} = .435.$$

Substituting into equation (6.4),

$$\sum_{i=1}^{10}(y_i - rx_i)^2 = \sum_{i=1}^{10} y_i^2 + r^2 \sum_{i=1}^{10} x_i^2 - 2r \sum_{i=1}^{10} x_i y_i$$

$$= .006224 + (.0566)^2(1.9035) - 2(.0566)(.10839)$$

$$= .000052285.$$

Then the bound on the error of estimation is

$$2\sqrt{\hat{V}(\hat{\tau}_y)} = 2\sqrt{\tau_x^2 \left(\frac{1}{n}\right)\left(\frac{1}{\bar{x}^2}\right) \frac{\sum\limits_{i=1}^{n}(y_i - rx_i)^2}{n - 1}}$$

$$= 2\sqrt{(1800)^2 \left(\frac{1}{10}\right) \frac{1}{(.435)^2}\left(\frac{.000052285}{9}\right)}$$

$$= 6.308.$$

To summarize, the ratio estimate of the total sugar content of the truck load of oranges is $\hat{\tau}_y = 101.79$ pounds with a bound on the error of estimation of 6.308. We are confident that the total sugar content, τ_y, lies in the interval

$$101.79 \pm 6.308,$$

that is, the interval 95.482 to 108.098 pounds.

You will recall that the population size, N, is frequently known. Consequently, the investigator must decide under what conditions use of the ratio estimator, $\hat{\tau}_y = r\tau_x$ is better than use of the corresponding estimator $\hat{\tau}_y = N\bar{y}$, where both estimators are based on simple random sampling (see Section 6.5). Generally, $r\tau_x$ possesses a smaller variance than $N\bar{y}$ when there is a strong, positive correlation between x and y (where ρ, the correlation coefficient between x and y, is greater than 1/2). Intuitively, this makes sense because in ratio estimation we are using the additional information provided by the subsidiary variable, x.

If an investigator is interested in a population mean rather than a population total, the corresponding ratio estimation procedure is shown in equations (6.8), (6.9), and (6.10).

Ratio estimator of a population mean μ_y:

$$\hat{\mu}_y = \frac{\sum\limits_{i=1}^{n} y_i}{\sum\limits_{i=1}^{n} x_i}(\mu_x) = r\mu_x. \qquad (6.8)$$

Estimated variance of $\hat{\mu}_y$:

$$\hat{V}(\hat{\mu}_y) = \mu_x^2 \hat{V}(r) = \mu_x^2 \left(\frac{N-n}{nN}\right)\left(\frac{1}{\mu_x^2}\right)\frac{\sum\limits_{i=1}^{n}(y_i - rx_i)^2}{n-1}. \qquad (6.9)$$

Bound on the error of estimation:

$$2\sqrt{\hat{V}(\hat{\mu}_y)} = 2\sqrt{\left(\frac{N-n}{nN}\right)\frac{\sum\limits_{i=1}^{n}(y_i - rx_i)^2}{n-1}}. \qquad (6.10)$$

Note that we do not need to know τ_x or N to estimate μ_y using the ratio procedure; however, we must know μ_x.

Example 6.3

A company wishes to estimate the average amount of money, μ_y, paid to employees for medical expenses, during the first three months of the current calendar year. Average quarterly figures are available in the fiscal reports of the previous year. A random sample of 100 employee records is taken from the population of 1000 employees. The sample results are summarized below. Use the data to estimate μ_y and to place a bound on the error of estimation.

$$n = 100, \qquad N = 1000$$

Total for the current quarter:

$$\sum_{i=1}^{100} y_i = 1750.$$

Total for the corresponding quarter of the previous year:

$$\sum_{i=1}^{100} x_i = 1200.$$

Population total, τ_x, for the corresponding quarter of the previous year:

$$\tau_x = 12500.$$

$$\sum_{i=1}^{100} y_i^2 = 30650, \qquad \sum_{i=1}^{100} x_i^2 = 15620, \qquad \sum_{i=1}^{100} y_i x_i = 21859.35.$$

Solution

The estimate of μ_y is

$$\hat{\mu}_y = r\mu_x,$$

where

$$\mu_x = \frac{\tau_x}{N} = \frac{12500}{1000} = 12.5.$$

Then,

$$\hat{\mu}_y = \frac{\sum\limits_{i=1}^{100} y_i}{\sum\limits_{i=1}^{100} x_i} (\mu_x) = \frac{1750}{1200}(12.5) = 18.23.$$

The bound on the error of estimation can be found using equation (6.10); however, we must first calculate

$$\sum_{i=1}^{100}(y_i - rx_i)^2 = \sum_{i=1}^{100}y_i^2 + r^2\sum_{i=1}^{100}x_i^2 - 2r\sum_{i=1}^{100}y_ix_i.$$

$$= 30650 + (1.4583)^2(15620) - (2.9166)(21889.35)$$

$$= 63868.099 - 63842.478$$

$$= 25.62125 \approx 25.62.$$

Substituting into equation (6.10), the bound on the error of estimation is

$$2\sqrt{\hat{V}(\hat{\mu}_y)} = 2\sqrt{\left(\frac{N-n}{nN}\right)\frac{\sum_{i=1}^{n}(y_i - rx_i)^2}{n-1}}$$

$$= 2\sqrt{\frac{1000-100}{100(1000)}\left(\frac{25.62}{99}\right)}$$

$$= .0965.$$

Thus, we estimate the average amount of money paid to employees for medical expenses to be \$18.23. We are very confident that the error for estimating μ_y is less than \$0.10.

To remember the formulas associated with ratio estimation of a population mean, total, or ratio, we make the following associations. The sample ratio, r, is given by the formula,

$$r = \frac{\sum_{i=1}^{n}y_i}{\sum_{i=1}^{n}x_i}. \tag{6.11}$$

The estimators of R, τ_y, and μ_y are then:

$$\hat{R} = r, \tag{6.12}$$

$$\hat{\tau}_y = r\tau_x, \tag{6.13}$$

and

$$\hat{\mu}_y = r\mu_x. \tag{6.14}$$

Thus, one need know only the formula for r and its relationship to $\hat{\mu}_y$ and $\hat{\tau}_y$.

Approximate variances can be obtained if you remember the basic formula,

$$\hat{V}(r) = \left(\frac{N-n}{nN}\right)\left(\frac{1}{\mu_x^2}\right)\frac{\sum\limits_{i=1}^{n}(y_i - rx_i)^2}{n-1}. \tag{6.15}$$

Thus,

$$\hat{V}(\hat{\tau}_y) = \tau_x^2\,\hat{V}(r), \tag{6.16}$$

and

$$\hat{V}(\hat{\mu}_y) = \mu_x^2\,\hat{V}(r). \tag{6.17}$$

6.4   Selecting the Sample Size

We stated previously that the amount of information contained in the sample depends upon the variation in the data (which is frequently controlled by the sample survey design) and the number of observations, n, included in the sample. Once the sampling procedure (design) has been chosen, the investigator must determine the number of elements to be drawn. We shall consider the sample size required to estimate a population parameter R, μ_y, or τ_y to within B units for simple random sampling using ratio estimators.

Note that the procedure for choosing the sample size, n, is identical to that presented in Section 4.5. The number of observations required to estimate R, a population ratio, with a bound on the error of estimation of magnitude B is determined by setting two standard deviations of the ratio estimator, r, equal to B and solving this expression for n. That is, we must solve

$$2\sqrt{V(r)} = B \tag{6.18}$$

for n. Although we have not discussed the form of $V(r)$, you recall that $\hat{V}(r)$, the estimated variance of r, is given by the formula

$$\hat{V}(r) = \left(\frac{N-n}{nN}\right)\left(\frac{1}{\mu_x^2}\right)\sum_{i=1}^{n}\frac{(y_i - rx_i)^2}{n-1}. \tag{6.19}$$

We can rewrite (6.19) as

$$\hat{V}(r) = \left(\frac{N-n}{nN}\right)\left(\frac{1}{\mu_x^2}\right)s^2. \tag{6.20}$$

In this instance we define

$$s^2 = \frac{\sum\limits_{i=1}^{n} (y_i - rx_i)^2}{n-1}.$$

An approximate population variance, $V(r)$, can be obtained from $\hat{V}(r)$ by replacing s^2 with the corresponding population variance σ^2. Thus, the number of observations required to estimate R with a bound, B, on the error of estimation is determined by solving the following equation for n:

$$2\sqrt{V(r)} = 2\sqrt{\left(\frac{N-n}{nN}\right)\left(\frac{1}{\mu_x^2}\right)\sigma^2} = B. \qquad (6.21)$$

Sample size required to estimate R with a bound on the error of estimation, B:

$$n = \frac{N\sigma^2}{ND + \sigma^2}, \qquad (6.22)$$

where

$$D = \frac{B^2\mu_x^2}{4}.$$

In a practical situation we are faced with a problem in determining the appropriate sample size because we do not know σ^2. If no past information is available to calculate s^2 as an estimate of σ^2, we take a preliminary sample of size n' and compute

$$\hat{\sigma}^2 = \frac{\sum\limits_{i=1}^{n'} (y_i - rx_i)^2}{n'-1}.$$

Then, we substitute this quantity for σ^2 in equation (6.22), and we find an *approximate* sample size. If μ_x is also unknown, it can be replaced by the sample mean, $\bar{x}$, calculated from the n' preliminary observations.

Example 6.4

A manufacturing company wishes to estimate the ratio of change from last year to this year in the number of man hours lost due to sickness. A preliminary study of $n' = 10$ employee records is made, and the results are tabulated below:

Employee	Man hours lost in previous year (x)	Man hours lost in current year (y)
1	12	13
2	24	25
3	15	15
4	30	32
5	32	36
6	26	24
7	10	12
8	15	16
9	0	2
10	14	12
	$\overline{178}$	$\overline{187}$

The company records show that the total number of man hours lost because of sickness for the previous year was $\tau_x = 16{,}300$. Use the data to determine the sample size required to estimate R, the rate of change for the company, with a bound on the error of estimation of magnitude $B = 0.01$. Assume the company has 1000 employees ($N = 1000$).

Solution

First, we calculate an estimate of σ^2 using the data from the preliminary study. Thus,

$$\hat{\sigma}^2 = \frac{\sum\limits_{i=1}^{10} (y_i - rx_i)^2}{9},$$

where

$$\sum_{i=1}^{10} (y_i - rx_i)^2 = \sum_{i=1}^{10} y_i^2 + r^2 \sum_{i=1}^{10} x_i^2 - 2r \sum_{i=1}^{10} x_i y_i.$$

Next, from the given data we determine

$$\sum_{i=1}^{10} y_i^2 = (13)^2 + (25)^2 + \cdots + (12)^2 = 4463,$$

$$\sum_{i=1}^{10} x_i^2 = (12)^2 + (24)^2 + \cdots + (14)^2 = 4066,$$

$$\sum_{i=1}^{10} x_i y_i = (12)(13) + (24)(25) + \cdots + (14)(12) = 4245,$$

and

$$r = \frac{\sum\limits_{i=1}^{10} y_i}{\sum\limits_{i=1}^{10} x_i} = \frac{187}{178} = 1.05.$$

Hence,

$$\sum_{i=1}^{10} (y_i - rx_i)^2 = \sum_{i=1}^{10} y_i^2 + r^2 \sum_{i=1}^{10} x_i^2 - 2r \sum_{i=1}^{10} x_i y_i$$
$$= 4463 + (1.05)^2(4066) - 2(1.05)(4245)$$
$$= 31.265,$$

and

$$\hat{\sigma}^2 = \frac{\sum\limits_{i=1}^{10} (y_i - rx_i)^2}{9} = \frac{31.265}{9} = 3.474.$$

The required sample size can now be found using equation (6.22). Note that

$$\mu_x = \frac{\tau_x}{N} = \frac{16300}{1000} = 16.3,$$

and

$$D = \frac{B^2}{4} \mu_x^2 = \frac{(.01)^2(16.3)^2}{4} = .006642.$$

Thus,

$$n = \frac{N\hat{\sigma}^2}{ND + \hat{\sigma}^2} = \frac{1000(3.474)}{1000(.006642) + 3.474} = 343.416.$$

Therefore, we should sample approximately 344 employee records to estimate R, the rate of change in man hours lost due to sickness, with a bound on the error of estimation of 0.01 hours.

Similarly, we can determine the number of observations, n, needed to estimate a population mean, μ_y, with a bound on the error of estimation of magnitude B. The required sample size is found by solving the following equation for n:

$$2\sqrt{V(\hat{\mu}_y)} = B. \tag{6.23}$$

Stated differently,

$$2\mu_x \sqrt{V(r)} = B \quad \text{(from equation (6.17))}.$$

The solution is shown in equation (6.24).

Sample size required to estimate μ_y with a bound on the error of estimation, B:

$$n = \frac{N\sigma^2}{ND + \sigma^2},\qquad(6.24)$$

where

$$D = \frac{B^2}{4}.$$

Note that we need not know the value of μ_x to determine n in equation (6.24); however, we do need an estimate of σ^2, either from prior information if it is available or from information obtained in a preliminary study.

Example 6.5

An investigator wishes to estimate the average number of trees, μ_y, per acre on a $N = 1000$ acre plantation. He plans to sample n one-acre plots and count the number of trees, y, on each plot. He also has aerial photographs of the plantation from which he can estimate the number of trees, x, on each plot for the entire plantation. Hence he knows μ_x. Therefore it seems appropriate to use a ratio estimator of μ_y. Determine the sample size needed to estimate μ_y with a bound on the error of estimation of magnitude $B = 1.0$.

Solution

Assuming no prior information is available, we must conduct a preliminary study to estimate σ^2. Since an investigator can readily examine ten one-acre plots in a day to determine the total number of trees, y, per plot, it is convenient to conduct a preliminary study of $n' = 10$ plots. The results of such a study are tabulated below with the corresponding aerial estimates, x:

Plot	Aerial estimate (x)	Actual number (y)
1	23	25
2	14	15
3	20	22
4	25	24
5	12	13
6	18	18
7	30	35
8	27	30
9	8	10
10	31	29
	208	221

An estimate of σ^2 is given by

$$\hat{\sigma}^2 = \sum_{i=1}^{10} \frac{(y_i - rx_i)^2}{9}.$$

Using equation (6.4),

$$\sum_{i=1}^{10} (y_i - rx_i)^2 = \sum_{i=1}^{10} y_i^2 + r^2 \sum_{i=1}^{10} x_i^2 - 2r \sum_{i=1}^{10} x_i y_i.$$

From the preliminary study,

$$\sum_{i=1}^{10} y_i^2 = (25)^2 + (15)^2 + \cdots + (29)^2 = 5469,$$

$$\sum_{i=1}^{10} x_i^2 = (23)^2 + (14)^2 + \cdots + (31)^2 = 4872,$$

$$\sum_{i=1}^{10} x_i y_i = (23)(25) + (14)(15) + \cdots + (31)(29) = 5144,$$

and

$$r = \frac{\sum_{i=1}^{10} y_i}{\sum_{i=1}^{10} x_i} = \frac{221}{208} = 1.06.$$

Thus,

$$\sum_{i=1}^{10} (y_i - rx_i)^2 = \sum_{i=1}^{10} y_i^2 + r^2 \sum_{i=1}^{10} x_i^2 - 2r \sum_{i=1}^{10} x_i y_i$$

$$= 5469 + (1.06)^2(4872) - 2(1.06)(5144)$$

$$= 37.8992,$$

and

$$\hat{\sigma}^2 = \sum_{i=1}^{10} \frac{(y_i - rx_i)^2}{9} = \frac{37.8992}{9} = 4.21.$$

We now determine n from equation (6.24):

$$n = \frac{N\sigma^2}{ND + \sigma^2} \quad \left(\text{where } D = \frac{B^2}{4} = \frac{1}{4} \right)$$

$$= \frac{100(4.21)}{1000(.25) + 4.21}$$

$$= 16.56.$$

To summarize, we need to examine approximately 17 plots to estimate μ_y, the average number of trees per one-acre plot with a bound on the error of estimation $B = 1.0$. We only need seven additional observations since we have ten from the preliminary study.

The sample size required to estimate τ_y with a bound on the error of estimation of magnitude B can be found by solving the following expression for n:

$$2\sqrt{V(\hat{\tau}_y)} = B \tag{6.25}$$

or, equivalently,

$$2\tau_x\sqrt{V(r)} = B \quad \text{(from equation (6.16))}.$$

Sample size required to estimate τ_y with a bound on the error of estimation B:

$$n = \frac{N\sigma^2}{ND + \sigma^2}$$

where

$$D = \frac{B^2}{4N^2}. \tag{6.26}$$

Example 6.6

An auditor wishes to compare the actual dollar value of an inventory of a hospital, τ_y, with the recorded inventory, τ_x. The recorded inventory, τ_x, can be summarized from computer-stored hospital records. The actual inventory, τ_y, could be determined by examining and counting all hospital supplies, but this process would be very time consuming and costly. Hence, the auditor plans to estimate τ_y based on a sample of n different items randomly selected from the hospital's supplies.

Records in the computer list $N = 2100$ different item types and the number of each particular item in the hospital inventory. Using these data a total value for each item, x, can be obtained by multiplying the total number of each recorded item by the unit value per item. The total dollar value of the inventory obtained from the computer is given by

τ_x = sum of the dollar values for the $N = 2100$ items

$$= \sum_{i=1}^{2100} x_i.$$

In this instance τ_x was found to be \$950,000. Determine the sample size (number of items) needed to estimate τ_y with a bound on the error of estimation of magnitude $B = \$500$.

Solution

Because there is no prior information available, a preliminary study must be conducted to estimate σ^2. Two men can determine the actual dollar value, y, for each of 15 items in one day. For this example, we shall use the data from a single day's inventory ($n' = 15$) as a preliminary study to obtain a rough estimate of σ^2 and consequently a rough approximation of the required sample size, n. Actually, the investigator would probably take a preliminary study of two or three days' inventory to provide a good approximation to σ^2 and hence, n; however, to simplify computations, we will consider a preliminary study of $n' = 15$ items. These data are summarized below along with the corresponding computer figures (entries in hundreds of dollars).

Item	Dollar value from computer (x)	Actual dollar value (y)
1	15.0	14.0
2	9.5	9.0
3	14.2	12.5
4	20.5	22.0
5	6.7	6.3
6	9.8	8.4
7	25.7	28.5
8	12.6	10.0
9	15.1	14.4
10	30.9	28.2
11	7.3	15.5
12	28.6	26.3
13	14.7	13.1
14	20.5	19.5
15	10.9	9.8
	$\overline{242.0}$	$\overline{237.5}$

To determine an estimate of σ^2, we must calculate

$$\sum_{i=1}^{15} (y_i - rx_i)^2 = \sum_{i=1}^{15} y_i^2 + r^2 \sum_{i=1}^{15} x_i^2 - 2r \sum_{i=1}^{15} x_i y_i.$$

Using the data from the preliminary study,

$$\sum_{i=1}^{15} y_i^2 = (14.0)^2 + (9.0)^2 + \cdots + (9.8)^2 = 4522.19,$$

$$\sum_{i=1}^{15} x_i^2 = (15.0)^2 + (9.5)^2 + \cdots + (10.9)^2 = 4706.54,$$

$$\sum_{i=1}^{15} x_i y_i = (15.0)(14.0) + (9.5)(9.0) + \cdots + (10.9)(9.8) = 4560.27,$$

and

$$r = \frac{\sum_{i=1}^{15} y_i}{\sum_{i=1}^{15} x_i} = \frac{237.5}{242} = .9814 \approx .98.$$

Thus,

$$\sum_{i=1}^{15} (y_i - rx_i)^2 = \sum_{i=1}^{15} y_i^2 + r^2 \sum_{i=1}^{15} x_i^2 - 2r \sum_{i=1}^{15} x_i y_i$$

$$= 4522.19 + (.98)^2(4706.54) - 2(.98)(4560.27)$$

$$= 104.2218,$$

and

$$\hat{\sigma}^2 = \sum_{i=1}^{15} \frac{(y_i - rx_i)^2}{14} = \frac{104.2218}{14} = 7.4444.$$

The required sample size now can can be found using equation (6.26). We have

$$D = \frac{B^2}{4N^2} = \frac{(500)^2}{4(2100)^2} = .01417$$

and hence

$$n = \frac{N\sigma^2}{ND + \sigma^2}$$

$$= \frac{2100(7.4444)}{2100(.01417) + 7.4444} = 420.2326.$$

Thus, the auditor must sample approximately 421 items to estimate τ_y, the actual dollar value of the inventory, to within $B = \$500$.

6.5 When to Use Ratio Estimation

Use of the ratio estimator is most effective when the relationship between the response, y, and a subsidiary variable, x, is linear through the origin and the variance of y is proportional to x. The following example illustrates this point. An automobile-tire distributor wishes to estimate the average cash receipts for his 1570 stores ($N = 1570$) during a particular sales period. From a simple random sample of $n = 50$ stores the corresponding cash receipts y_i ($i = 1, 2, \ldots, 50$) are observed. One possible estimator of μ_y, the average cash receipts for the company, is $\bar{y}$, the sample mean.

In addition to obtaining cash receipts y_i, suppose the distributor can also obtain x_i ($i = 1, 2, \ldots, 50$), the number of customers who made purchases in store i during the sales period. To determine the relationship between y and x, one can plot the sales and customer data for the $n = 50$ sampled stores.

If the plot is similar to the one presented in Figure 6.1, we can assume that

Figure 6.1

the cash receipts, y, are linearly related to the number of customers purchasing goods, x. In fact, we could depict this relationship with a straight line passing through the intersection of the x and y axes, and hence we can say it is linear through the origin. In addition you will note from Figure 6.1 that the "scatter" of y-values widens as x increases. Hence, we can say that the variance of y is proportional to x. Under these conditions the ratio estimator of μ_y, the average amount of cash receipts per store, should have a smaller variance and, hence, be more precise than $\bar{y}$.

Sometimes a plot of y versus x does not clearly indicate that ratio estimation should be used. The strength of the correlation ρ between y and x is another good indicator of the effectiveness of the ratio estimator. For $\rho > 1/2$, the ratio estimator should provide a more precise estimate of μ_y or τ_y than would $\bar{y}$ or $N\bar{y}$.

Unlike the estimation procedures discussed previously, ratio estimation usually leads to biased estimators. Thus, we must consider the magnitude of the bias to decide which estimation procedure to use. Although there are no exact formulas to determine the bias of these estimators, it can be shown that the absolute value of the bias is less than or equal to the product of the standard deviation of the sample mean of the subsidiary variable x and the standard deviation of the ratio estimator, all divided by μ_x. That is,

$$|E(\hat{\theta}) - \theta| \leq \frac{\sigma_{\bar{x}}\sigma_{\hat{\theta}}}{\mu_x}, \qquad (6.27)$$

where $\hat{\theta}$ can be the ratio estimator r, $\hat{\mu}_y$, or $\hat{\tau}_y$, and θ is the corresponding parameter estimated. If estimates of $\sigma_{\bar{x}}$, $\sigma_{\hat{\theta}}$, and μ_x are known from prior experimentation, one can estimate the maximum bias for a given physical situation by using equation (6.27).

Generally, for a large sample size ($n > 30$) and for $(\sigma_{\bar{x}}/\mu_x) \leq .10$, the bias is negligible. Note also that ratio estimators are unbiased when the relationship between y and x is linear through the origin.

Finally, we must consider the cost of obtaining information on the subsidiary variable x. If the physical situation suggests the use of ratio estimation, the experimenter must decide if the increased precision of the ratio estimator justifies the additional cost.

6.6   Summary

This chapter has briefly presented ratio estimation of a population mean, total, and ratio for simple random sampling. By measuring a variable, y, and a subsidiary variable, x, on each element in the sample, we obtain additional information for estimating the population parameter of interest. When a strong positive relationship exists between the variables x and y, the ratio estimation procedure usually provides more precise estimators of μ_y and τ_y than do the standard techniques presented in Chapter 4.

Sample size requirements are presented for estimating μ_y, τ_y, and R with a bound on the error of estimation equal to B. In each case, it is necessary to obtain an estimate of σ^2 from prior information or from a preliminary study to approximate the required sample size.

Ratio estimation can be used with simple random sampling, stratified random sampling, or other types of survey designs. It is essential to remember that one must be able to measure two highly correlated variables, x and y, on each element of the sample.

This chapter demonstrates relevant concepts of ratio estimation for the simplest type of survey design, simple random sampling. Application of ratio estimation for stratified random sampling is beyond the scope of this text. References for the interested reader are provided at the end of this chapter.

References

Cochran, W. G., *Sampling Techniques*, 2d ed., New York: John Wiley and Sons, Inc., 1953.

Hansen, M. H., W. N. Hurwitz, and W. G. Madow, *Sample Survey Methods and Theory*, Vol. 1, New York: John Wiley and Sons, Inc., 1953.

Kish, L., *Survey Sampling*, New York: John Wiley and Sons, Inc., 1965.

Mendenhall, W., *Introduction to Probability and Statistics*, 3d ed. Belmont, Calif.: Wadsworth Publishing Company, Inc., 1971.

Exercises

6.1   A forester is interested in estimating the total volume of trees in a timber sale. He records the volume for each tree in a simple random sample. In addition he measures the basal area for each tree marked for sale. He then uses a ratio estimator of total volume.

The forester decides to take a simple random sample of $n = 12$ from the $N = 250$ trees marked for sale. Let x denote basal area and y the cubic foot volume for a tree. The total basal area for all 250 trees, τ_x, is 75 square feet. Use the data below to estimate τ_y, the total cubic foot volume for those trees marked for sale, and place a bound on the error of estimation.

Tree sampled	Basal area (x)	Cubic foot volume (y)
1	.3	6
2	.5	9
3	.4	7
4	.9	19
5	.7	15
6	.2	5
7	.6	12
8	.5	9
9	.8	20
10	.4	9
11	.8	18
12	.6	13

6.2   Use the y-data in Exercise 6.1 to compute an estimate of τ_y using $N\bar{y}$. Place a bound on the error of estimation. Compare your results to those obtained in Exercise 6.1.

6.3   A consumer survey was conducted to determine the ratio of the money spent on food to the total income per year for households in a small community. A simple random sample of 14 households was selected from 150 in the community. Sample data are tabulated below. Estimate R, the population ratio, and place a bound on the error of estimation.

Household	x_i (Total income)	y_i (Amount spent on food)
1	5,010	990
2	12,240	2,524
3	9,600	1,935
4	15,600	3,123
5	14,400	2,760
6	6,500	1,337
7	8,700	1,756
8	8,200	2,132
9	14,600	3,504
10	12,700	2,286
11	11,500	2,875
12	10,600	2,226
13	7,700	1,463
14	8,500	1,905

6.4   A corporation is interested in estimating the total earnings from sales of color television sets at the end of a given three month period. The total earnings figures are available for all districts within the corporation for the corresponding three month period of the previous year. A simple random sample of 13 district offices is selected from the 123 offices within the corporation. Using a ratio estimator, estimate τ_y and place a bound on the error of estimation. Use the data in the table below and take $\tau_x = 128{,}200$.

Office	Three month data from previous year (x_i)	Three month data from current year (y_i)
1	550	610
2	720	780
3	1,500	1,600
4	1,020	1,030
5	620	600
6	980	1,050
7	928	977
8	1,200	1,440
9	1,350	1,570
10	1,750	2,210
11	670	980
12	729	865
13	1,530	1,710

6.5   Use the data in Exercise 6.4 to estimate the mean earnings for offices within the corporation. Place a bound on the error of estimation.

6.6 An investigator has a colony of $N = 763$ rats which have been subjected to a standard drug. The average length of time to thread a maze correctly under influence of the standard drug was found to be $\mu_x = 17.2$ seconds. The investigator now would like to subject a random sample of 11 rats to a new drug. Estimate the average time required to thread the maze while under the influence of the new drug. Place a bound on the error of estimation. (*Hint:* It is reasonable to employ a ratio estimator for μ_y if we assume that the rats will react to the new drug in much the same way as they did the standard drug.)

Rat	Standard drug (x_i)	New drug (y_i)
1	14.3	15.2
2	15.7	16.1
3	17.8	18.1
4	17.5	17.6
5	13.2	14.5
6	18.8	19.4
7	17.6	17.5
8	14.3	14.1
9	14.9	15.2
10	17.9	18.1
11	19.2	19.5

6.7 A group of 100 rabbits is being used in a nutrition study. A pre-study weight is recorded for each rabbit. The average of these weights is 3.1 pounds. After two months the experimenter wants to obtain a rough approximation of the average weight of the rabbits. He selects $n = 10$ rabbits at random and weighs them. The original weights and current weights are presented below:

Rabbit	1	2	3	4	5	6	7	8	9	10
Original weight	3.2	3.0	2.9	2.8	2.8	3.1	3.0	3.2	2.9	2.8
Current weight	4.1	4.0	4.1	3.9	3.7	4.1	4.2	4.1	3.9	3.8

Estimate the average current weight, and place a bound on the error of estimation.

6.8 A social worker wants to estimate the ratio of the average number of rooms per apartment to the average number of people per apartment in an urban ghetto area. He selects a simple random sample of 25 apartments from the 275 in the ghetto area. Let x_i denote the number of people in apartment i, and let y_i denote the number of rooms in apartment i. From a count of the number of rooms and number of people in each apartment, the following data are obtained:

$$\bar{x} = 9.2 \qquad\qquad \bar{y} = 2.6$$

$$\sum_{i=1}^{25} x_i^2 = 2116.0 \qquad \sum_{i=1}^{25} x_i y_i = 522 \qquad \sum_{i=1}^{25} y_i^2 = 169.0$$

Estimate the ratio of average number of rooms to average number of people for this area, and place a bound on the error of estimation.

6.9   A forest resource manager is interested in estimating the number of dead
       fir trees in a 300 acre area of heavy infestation. Using an aerial photo, he di-
       vides the area into 200 one and a half acre plots. Let x denote the photo
       count of dead firs and y the actual ground count for a simple random
       sample of $n = 10$ plots. The total number of dead fir trees obtained from
       the photo count is $\tau_x = 4200$. Use the sample data below to estimate τ_y, the
       total number of dead firs in the 300 acre area. Place a bound on the error
       of estimation.

Plot sampled	Photo count (x_i)	Ground count (y_i)
1	12	18
2	30	42
3	24	24
4	24	36
5	18	24
6	30	36
7	12	14
8	6	10
9	36	48
10	42	54

6.10   Members of a teachers' association are concerned about the salary in-
       creases given to high school teachers in a particular school system. A
       simple random sample of $n = 15$ teachers is selected from an alphabetical
       listing of all high school teachers in the system. All 15 teachers are inter-
       viewed to determine their salaries for this year and the previous year.
       Use these data to estimate R, the rate of change, for $N = 750$ high school
       teachers in the community school system. Place a bound on the error of
       estimation.

Teacher	Past year's salary	Present year's salary
1	5400	5600
2	6700	6940
3	7792	8084
4	9956	10275
5	6355	6596
6	5108	5322
7	7891	8167
8	5216	5425
9	5416	5622
10	5397	5597
11	8152	8437
12	6436	6700
13	9192	9523
14	7006	7279
15	7311	7582

6.11   An experimenter was investigating a new food additive for cattle. Midway
       through the two month study, he was interested in estimating the average
       weight for the entire herd of $N = 500$ steers. A simple random sample of

$n = 12$ steers was selected from the herd and weighed. These data and pre-study weights are presented below for all cattle sampled. Assume μ_x, the pre-study average, was 880 lbs. Estimate μ_y, the average weight for the herd, and place a bound on the error of estimation.

Steer	Pre-study weight in pounds	Present weight in pounds
1	815	897
2	919	992
3	690	752
4	984	1093
5	200	768
6	260	828
7	1323	1428
8	1067	1152
9	789	875
10	573	642
11	834	909
12	1049	1122

6.12   An advertising firm is concerned about the effect of a new regional promotional campaign on the total dollar sales for a particular product. A simple random sample of $n = 20$ stores is drawn from the $N = 452$ regional stores in which the product is sold. Quarterly sales data are obtained for the current three month period and the three month period prior to the new campaign. Use these data to estimate τ_y, the total sales for the current period, and place a bound on the error of estimation. Assume $\tau_x = 216,256$.

Store	Pre-campaign sales	Present sales
1	208	239
2	400	428
3	440	472
4	259	276
5	351	363
6	880	942
7	273	294
8	487	514
9	183	195
10	863	897
11	599	626
12	510	538
13	828	888
14	473	510
15	924	998
16	110	171
17	829	889
18	257	265
19	388	419
20	244	257

6.13   Use the data of Exercise 6.12 to determine the sample size required to estimate τ_y, with a bound on the error of estimation equal to $3,800.

7
Cluster Sampling

7.1   Introduction

You will recall that the objective of sample survey design is to obtain a specified amount of information about a population parameter at minimum cost. Stratified random sampling is often better suited for this than is simple random sampling for the three reasons indicated in Section 5.1. This chapter introduces a third design, cluster sampling, which sometimes gives more information per unit cost than do either simple or stratified random sampling.

Definition 7.1   A *cluster sample* is a simple random sample in which each sampling unit is a collection, or cluster, of elements.

Cluster sampling is less costly than simple or stratified random sampling if the cost of obtaining a frame which lists all population elements is very high or if the cost of obtaining observations increases as the distance separating the elements increases.

To illustrate, suppose an experimenter wishes to estimate the average income per household in a large city. How should he choose the sample? If he uses simple random sampling, he will need a frame listing all households (elements) in the city and this may be very costly or impossible to obtain. He cannot avoid this problem by using stratified random sampling because a frame is still required for each stratum in the population. Rather than drawing a simple random sample of *elements*, the experimenter could divide the city into regions such as blocks (or clusters of elements), and select a simple random sample of blocks from the population. This is easily accomplished using a frame which lists all city blocks. Then the income of every household within each sampled block would be measured.

To illustrate the second reason for using cluster sampling, suppose that a list of households in the city is available. The experimenter could select a simple random sample of households, which probably would be scattered throughout the city. The cost of conducting interviews in the scattered households would be large due to the interviewer travel time and other related expenses. Stratified random sampling could lower these expenses, but using cluster sampling is a more effective method of reducing travel costs. Elements within a cluster should be close to each other geographically and, hence, travel expenses should be reduced. Obviously, travel within a city block would be minimal when compared to the travel associated with simple random sampling of households within the city.

To summarize, cluster sampling is an effective design for obtaining a specified amount of information at minimum cost when:

1. A good frame listing population elements either is not available or is very costly to obtain.
2. The cost of obtaining observations increases as the distance separating the elements increases.

7.2   How to Draw a Cluster Sample

The first task in cluster sampling is to specify appropriate clusters. Elements within a cluster are often physically close together and, hence, tend to have similar characteristics. Stated another way, the measurement on one element in a cluster may be highly correlated with the measurement on another. Thus, the amount of information pertinent to a population parameter may not be increased substantially as new measurements are taken within a cluster. Since measurements cost money, an experimenter would waste money by choosing too large a cluster size. As a general rule, the number of elements within a cluster should be small relative to the population size, and the number of clusters in the sample should be reasonably large. (This problem is discussed in more detail in Section 7.4.)

For example, suppose that school districts are specified as clusters for sampling households in a city. The clusters contain many households. Consequently, the resources of the experimenter allow only a small number of clusters, say 2 or 3, to be sampled. This sample may not be representative of the population because the households within the same school district may be relatively homogeneous with respect to the characteristic being measured. More information could be obtained by sampling a larger number of clusters of smaller size.

As another example, an experimenter wants to estimate the proportion of defective light bulbs produced by a certain factory. He could sample individual bulbs, packs containing a small number of bulbs, or cartons containing many packs. The experimenter must choose the appropriate cluster size to obtain the most information per unit cost. Sampling individual bulbs may be expensive and consequently not used. If the cost restrictions force the experimenter to choose between sampling a few cartons (2 or 3) or many packs (20 or 30), he should choose the latter scheme.

Once appropriate clusters have been specified, a frame which lists all clusters in the population must be composed. A simple random sample of clusters is then selected from this frame by using the methods of Section 4.2. We illustrate with the following example.

Example 7.1

A sociologist wants to estimate the average income per adult male in a certain small city. No list of resident adults is available. How should he design the sample survey?

Solution

Cluster sampling seems to be the logical choice for the survey design because no list of elements (adult males) is available. The city is marked off into rectangular blocks, except for two industrial areas and three parks which contain only a few houses. It is decided that each of the city blocks will be considered one cluster, the two industrial areas will be considered one cluster, and finally the three parks will be considered one cluster. The clusters are numbered on a city map, with the numbers from 1 to 415. The experimenter has enough time and money to sample $n = 25$ clusters and to interview every adult male living within each cluster. Hence, 25 random numbers between 1 and 415 are selected from Table 3 of the Appendix, and the clusters having these numbers are marked on the map. Interviewers are then assigned to each of the sampled clusters.

7.3   Estimation of a Population Mean and Total

Cluster sampling is simple random sampling with each sampling unit containing a number of elements. Hence, the estimators of the population mean, μ, and total, τ, are similar to those for simple random sampling. In particular, the sample mean, $\bar{y}$, is a good estimator of the population mean, μ. An estimator of μ and two estimators of τ are discussed in this section.

The following notation is used in this chapter:

N = the number of *clusters* in the population,

n = the number of clusters selected in a simple random sample,

m_i = the number of elements in cluster i, $i = 1, \ldots, N$,

$$\bar{m} = \frac{1}{n} \sum_{i=1}^{n} m_i = \text{the average cluster size for the sample,}$$

$$M = \sum_{i=1}^{N} m_i = \text{the number of elements in the population,}$$

$$\bar{M} = \frac{M}{N} = \text{the average cluster size for the population,}$$

y_i = the total of all observations in the ith cluster.

The estimator of the population mean, μ, is the sample mean, $\bar{y}$, which is given by

$$\bar{y} = \frac{\sum_{i=1}^{n} y_i}{\sum_{i=1}^{n} m_i}.$$

Thus, $\bar{y}$ takes the form of a ratio estimator, as developed in Chapter 6, with m_i taking the place of x_i. Then, the estimated variance of $\bar{y}$ has the form of the variance of a ratio estimator given by (6.2).

Estimator of the population mean μ:

$$\bar{y} = \frac{\sum_{i=1}^{n} y_i}{\sum_{i=1}^{n} m_i}. \tag{7.1}$$

Estimated variance of $\bar{y}$:

$$\hat{V}(\bar{y}) = \left(\frac{N-n}{Nn\bar{M}^2} \right) \frac{\sum_{i=1}^{n} (y_i - \bar{y}m_i)^2}{n-1}. \tag{7.2}$$

Bound on the error of estimation:

$$2\sqrt{\hat{V}(\bar{y})} = 2\sqrt{\left(\frac{N-n}{NnM^2}\right)\frac{\sum\limits_{i=1}^{n}(y_i - \bar{y}m_i)^2}{n-1}}.\qquad (7.3)$$

M can be estimated by $\bar{m}$ if M is unknown.

The estimated variance in equation (7.2) is biased and a good estimator of $V(\bar{y})$ only if n is large, say $n \geq 20$. The bias disappears if the cluster sizes $m_1, m_2, \ldots, m_N$, are equal.

Let us illustrate the use of the above formulas with an example.

Example 7.2

Interviews are conducted in each of the 25 blocks sampled in Example 7.1. The data on income for adult males are presented in Table 7.1. Use the data to estimate the average income per adult male in the city, and place a bound on the error of estimation.

Table 7.1 Incomes for adult males.

Cluster i	Number of adult males m_i	Total income per cluster y_i	Cluster i	Number of adult males m_i	Total income per cluster y_i
1	8	$ 96,000	14	10	$49,000
2	12	121,000	15	9	53,000
3	4	42,000	16	3	50,000
4	5	65,000	17	6	32,000
5	6	52,000	18	5	22,000
6	6	40,000	19	5	45,000
7	7	75,000	20	4	37,000
8	5	65,000	21	6	51,000
9	8	45,000	22	8	30,000
10	3	50,000	23	7	39,000
11	2	85,000	24	3	47,000
12	6	43,000	25	8	41,000
13	5	54,000	$\sum\limits_{i=1}^{25} m_i = 151$	$\sum\limits_{i=1}^{25} y_i = \$1,329,000$	

Solution

The best estimate of the population mean, μ, is given by (7.1) and calculated as follows:

$$\bar{y} = \frac{\sum\limits_{i=1}^{n} y_i}{\sum\limits_{i=1}^{n} m_i} = \frac{\$1,329,000}{151} = \$8,801.$$

In order to calculate $\hat{V}(\bar{y})$, we need the following quantities:

$$\sum_{i=1}^{n=25} y_i^2 = y_1^2 + y_2^2 + \cdots + y_{25}^2$$

$$= (96{,}000)^2 + (121{,}000)^2 + \cdots + (41{,}000)^2$$

$$= 82{,}039{,}000{,}000,$$

$$\sum_{i=1}^{n=25} m_i^2 = m_1^2 + m_2^2 + \cdots + m_{25}^2$$

$$= (8)^2 + (12)^2 + \cdots + (8)^2$$

$$= 1047,$$

and

$$\sum_{i=1}^{n=25} y_i m_i = y_1 m_1 + y_2 m_2 + \cdots + y_{25} m_{25}$$

$$= (96{,}000)(8) + (121{,}000)(12) + \cdots + (41{,}000)(8)$$

$$= 8{,}403{,}000.$$

The following equality is easily established:

$$\sum_{i=1}^{n} (y_i - \bar{y}m_i)^2 = \sum_{i=1}^{n} y_i^2 - 2\bar{y} \sum_{i=1}^{n} y_i m_i + \bar{y}^2 \sum_{i=1}^{n} m_i^2.$$

Substituting into this equation from Table 7.1,

$$\sum_{i=1}^{25} (y_i - \bar{y}m_i)^2 = 82{,}039{,}000{,}000 - 2(8{,}801)(8{,}403{,}000) + (8{,}801)^2(1047)$$

$$= 15{,}227{,}502{,}247.$$

Since M is not known, the $\bar{M}$ appearing in equation (7.2) must be estimated by $\bar{m}$, where

$$\bar{m} = \frac{\sum_{i=1}^{n} m_i}{n} = \frac{151}{25} = 6.04.$$

Example 7.1 gives $N = 415$. Then, from equation (7.2),

$$\hat{V}(\bar{y}) = \frac{N-n}{Nn\bar{M}^2} \cdot \frac{\sum_{i=1}^{n} (y_i - \bar{y}m_i)^2}{n-1}$$

$$= \frac{415 - 25}{(415)(25)(6.04)^2} \cdot \frac{(15{,}227{,}502{,}247)}{24} = 653{,}785.$$

Thus, the estimate of μ with a bound on the error of estimation is given by

$$\bar{y} \pm 2\sqrt{\hat{V}(\bar{y})},$$

$$8,801 \pm 2\sqrt{653,785},$$

or

$$8,801 \pm 1,617.$$

The best estimate of the average income per adult male is \$8,801, and the error of estimation should be less than \$1,617 with probability close to .95. This is a rather large bound on the error of estimation; and it could be reduced by sampling more clusters and, consequently, increasing the sampling size.

The population total, τ, is now $M\mu$ because M denotes the total number of elements in the population. Consequently, as in simple random sampling, $M\bar{y}$ provides an estimator of τ.

Estimator of the population total τ:

$$M\bar{y} = M \frac{\sum\limits_{i=1}^{n} y_i}{\sum\limits_{i=1}^{n} m_i}. \tag{7.4}$$

Estimated variance of $M\bar{y}$:

$$\hat{V}(M\bar{y}) = M^2 \hat{V}(\bar{y}) = N^2 \left(\frac{N-n}{Nn}\right) \frac{\sum\limits_{i=1}^{n}(y_i - \bar{y}m_i)^2}{n-1}. \tag{7.5}$$

Bound on the error of estimation:

$$2\sqrt{\hat{V}(M\bar{y})} = 2\sqrt{N^2\left(\frac{N-n}{Nn}\right)\frac{\sum\limits_{i=1}^{n}(y_i - \bar{y}m_i)^2}{n-1}}. \tag{7.6}$$

Note that the estimator $M\bar{y}$ is useful only if the number of elements in the population, M, is known.

Example 7.3

Use the data in Table 7.1 to estimate the total income of all adult males in the city, and place a bound on the error of estimation. There are 2,500 adult males in the city.

Solution

The sample mean, $\bar{y}$, is calculated to be $8,801 in Example 7.2. Thus, the estimate of τ is

$$M\bar{y} = 2500(8,801) = \$22,002,500.$$

The quantity $\hat{V}(\bar{y})$ is calculated by the method used in Example 7.2, except that $\bar{M}$ can now be used in place of $\bar{m}$. The estimate of τ with a bound on the error of estimation is

$$M\bar{y} \pm 2\sqrt{\hat{V}(M\bar{y})},$$

$$M\bar{y} \pm 2\sqrt{M^2 \hat{V}(\bar{y})},$$

$$22,002,500 \pm 2\sqrt{(2500)^2(657,242)},$$

or

$$22,002,500 \pm 4,053,522.$$

Again, this is a large bound on the error of estimation, and it could be reduced by increasing the sample size.

Often the number of elements in the population is not known in problems for which cluster sampling is appropriate. This makes it impossible to use the estimator $M\bar{y}$, but we can form another estimator of the population total which does not depend on M. The quantity $\bar{y}_t$, given by

$$\bar{y}_t = \frac{1}{n} \sum_{i=1}^{n} y_i, \tag{7.7}$$

is the average of the cluster totals for the n sampled clusters. Hence, $\bar{y}_t$ is an unbiased estimator of the average of the N cluster totals in the population. By the same reasoning as employed in Chapter 4, $N\bar{y}_t$ is an unbiased estimator of the sum of the cluster totals or, equivalently, of the population total, τ.

For example, it is highly unlikely that the number of adult males in a city would be known, and hence the estimator $N\bar{y}_t$, rather than $M\bar{y}$, would have to be used to estimate τ.

An estimator of the population total, τ, which does not depend on M:

$$N\bar{y}_t = \frac{N}{n} \sum_{i=1}^{n} y_i. \tag{7.8}$$

Estimated variance of $N\bar{y}_t$:

$$\hat{V}(N\bar{y}_t) = N^2 \hat{V}(\bar{y}_t) = N^2 \left(\frac{N-n}{Nn}\right) \frac{\sum_{i=1}^{n}(y_i - \bar{y}_t)^2}{n-1}. \tag{7.9}$$

Bound on the error of estimation:

$$2\sqrt{\hat{V}(N\bar{y}_t)} = 2\sqrt{N^2\left(\frac{N-n}{Nn}\right)\frac{\sum_{i=1}^{n}(y_i - \bar{y}_t)^2}{n-1}}. \tag{7.10}$$

If there is a large amount of variation among the cluster sizes and if cluster sizes are highly correlated with cluster totals, the variance of $N\bar{y}_t$ (equation (7.9)) is generally larger than the variance of $M\bar{y}$ (equation (7.5)). The estimator $N\bar{y}_t$ does not use the information provided by the cluster sizes $m_1, m_2, \ldots, m_n$, and, hence, may be less precise.

Example 7.4

Use the data of Table 7.1 to estimate the total income of all adult males in the city if M is not known. Place a bound on the error of estimation.

Solution

Example 7.1 gives $N = 415$. From equation (7.8) and Table 7.1 the estimate of the total income, τ, is

$$N\bar{y}_t = \frac{N}{n}\sum_{i=1}^{n} y_i$$

$$= \frac{415}{25}(1,329,000) = \$22,061,400.$$

This figure is fairly close to the estimate given in Example 7.3.

To place a bound on the error of estimation, we first calculate

$$\sum_{i=1}^{n} (y_i - \bar{y}_t)^2 = \sum_{i=1}^{n} y_i^2 - \frac{1}{n}\left(\sum_{i=1}^{n} y_i\right)^2$$

$$= 82{,}039{,}000{,}000 - \frac{1}{25}(1{,}329{,}000)^2$$

$$= 11{,}389{,}360{,}000.$$

Then the estimate of the total income of all adult males in the city, with a bound on the error of estimation, is

$$N\bar{y}_t \pm 2\sqrt{\hat{V}(N\bar{y}_t)}.$$

Substituting into equation (7.10), we calculate

$$N\bar{y}_t \pm 2\sqrt{N^2\left(\frac{N-n}{Nn}\right)\frac{\sum_{i=1}^{n}(y_i - \bar{y}_t)^2}{n-1}}$$

$$22{,}061{,}400 \pm 2\sqrt{(415)^2\left(\frac{415-25}{(415)(25)}\right)\frac{(11{,}389{,}360{,}000)}{24}},$$

or

$$22{,}061{,}400 \pm 3{,}505{,}920.$$

The bound on the error of estimation is slightly smaller than the bound for the estimator $M\bar{y}$ (Example 7.3). This is partly because the cluster sizes are not highly correlated with the cluster total in this example. In other words, the cluster sizes are providing little information on cluster totals; hence, the unbiased estimator $N\bar{y}_t$ appears to be better than the estimator $M\bar{y}$.

The estimators of μ and τ possess special properties when all cluster sizes are equal (that is, $m_1 = m_2 = \cdots = m_N$). First, the estimator $\bar{y}$, given by equation (7.1), is an unbiased estimator of the population mean, μ. Second, $\hat{V}(\bar{y})$, given by equation (7.2), is an unbiased estimator of the variance of $\bar{y}$. Finally, the two estimators, $M\bar{y}$ and $N\bar{y}_t$, of the population total, τ, are equivalent.

Example 7.5

The circulation manager of a newspaper wishes to estimate the average number of newspapers purchased per household in a given community. Travel costs from household to household are substantial. Therefore, the 4000 households in the community are listed in 400 geographical clusters of 10 households each, and a simple random sample of 4 clusters is selected. Interviews are conducted with the following results:

Cluster	Number of Newspapers	Total
1	1 2 1 3 3 2 1 4 1 1	19
2	1 3 2 2 3 1 4 1 1 2	20
3	2 1 1 1 1 3 2 1 3 1	16
4	1 1 3 2 1 5 1 2 3 1	20

Estimate the average number of newspapers per household for the community, and place a bound on the error of estimation.

Solution

From equation (7.1),

$$\bar{y} = \frac{\sum\limits_{i=1}^{n} y_i}{\sum\limits_{i=1}^{n} m_i}.$$

When $m_1 = m_2 = \cdots = m_n = m$ the equation becomes

$$\bar{y} = \frac{\sum\limits_{i=1}^{n} y_i}{nm} = \frac{19 + 20 + 16 + 20}{4(10)} = 1.875.$$

Also, it is easily shown that

$$\sum_{i=1}^{n} (y_i - \bar{y}m_i)^2 = \sum_{i=1}^{n} y_i^2 - 2\bar{y}\sum_{i=1}^{n} y_i m_i + \bar{y}^2 \sum_{i=1}^{n} m_i^2$$

$$= \sum_{i=1}^{n} y_i^2 - nm^2\bar{y}^2.$$

Substituting, we obtain

$$\sum_{i=1}^{n} (y_i - \bar{y}m_i)^2 = (19)^2 + (20)^2 + (16)^2 + (20)^2 - 4(10)^2(1.875)^2$$

$$= 10.75.$$

Thus, from equation (7.2),

$$\hat{V}(\bar{y}) = \frac{N-n}{Nn\bar{M}^2} \frac{\sum\limits_{i=1}^{n}(y_i - \bar{y}m_i)^2}{n-1}$$

$$= \frac{(400-4)(10.75)}{400(4)(10)^2(3)}$$

$$= .0089.$$

Therefore, the best estimate of the average number of newspapers per household with a bound on the error of estimation is

$$\bar{y} \pm 2\sqrt{\hat{V}(\bar{y})},$$

$$1.875 \pm 2\sqrt{.0089},$$

or

$$1.875 \pm .188.$$

Thus, the estimate of the average number of newspapers per household is 1.875 with a high probability that the error of estimation is less than .188.

7.4   Selecting the Sample Size for Estimating Population Means and Totals

The quantity of information in a cluster sample is affected by two factors, the number of clusters and the relative cluster size. We have not encountered the latter factor in any of the sampling procedures discussed previously. In the problem of estimating the number of homes with inadequate fire insurance in a state, the clusters could be counties, voting districts, school districts, communities, or any other convenient grouping of homes. We will assume that the relative cluster size has been selected in advance and will consider the problem of choosing the number of clusters, n.

From equation (7.2), the estimated variance of $\bar{y}$ is

$$\hat{V}(\bar{y}) = \frac{N - n}{Nn\overline{M}^2} s_c^2,$$

where

$$s_c^2 = \frac{\sum_{i=1}^{n} (y_i - \bar{y}m_i)^2}{n - 1}. \tag{7.11}$$

The actual variance of $\bar{y}$ is approximately

$$V(\bar{y}) = \frac{N - n}{Nn\overline{M}^2} \sigma_c^2, \tag{7.12}$$

where σ_c^2 is the population quantity estimated by s_c^2.

Because we do not know σ_c^2 or the average cluster size, $\overline{M}$, choice of the sample size, that is, the number of clusters necessary to purchase a specified quantity of information concerning a population parameter, is difficult. We overcome this difficulty by using the same method as we used for ratio estimation. That is, we use an estimate of σ_c^2 and $\overline{M}$ available from a prior survey or we select a preliminary sample containing n' elements. Estimates of σ_c^2 and $\overline{M}$ can be computed from the preliminary sample and used to acquire an approximate total sample size, n. Thus, as in all problems of selecting a sample size, we equate two standard deviations of our estimator to a bound on the error of estimation, B. This bound is chosen by the experimenter and represents the maximum error that he is willing to tolerate. That is,

$$2\sqrt{V(\bar{y})} = B.$$

Using equation (7.12), we can solve for n.

We obtain similar results when using $M\bar{y}$ to estimate the population total, τ, because $V(M\bar{y}) = M^2 V(\bar{y})$.

The approximate sample size required to estimate μ with a bound, B, on the error of estimation:

$$n = \frac{N\sigma_c^2}{ND + \sigma_c^2},\qquad (7.13)$$

where σ_c^2 is estimated by s_c^2 and

$$D = \frac{B^2 \overline{M}^2}{4}.$$

Example 7.6

Suppose the data in Table 7.2 represent a preliminary sample of incomes in the city. How large a sample should be taken in a future survey in order to estimate the average income per adult male, μ, with a bound of $500 on the error of estimation?

Solution

To use equation (7.13), σ_c^2 must be estimated; the best estimate available is s_c^2, which can be calculated using the data in Table 7.1. Using the calculations in Example 7.2,

$$s_c^2 = \frac{\sum_{i=1}^{n}(y_i - \bar{y}m_i)^2}{n-1} = \frac{15,227,502,247}{24}$$

$$= 634,479,260.$$

$\bar{M}$ can be estimated by $\bar{m} = 6.04$ calculated from Table 7.1. Then D is approximately

$$\frac{B^2 \bar{m}^2}{4} = \frac{(500)^2 (6.04)^2}{4} = (62{,}500)(6.04)^2.$$

Using equation (7.13),

$$n = \frac{N\sigma_c^2}{ND + \sigma_c^2}$$

$$= \frac{415(634{,}479{,}260)}{415(6.04)^2(62{,}500) + 634{,}479{,}260}$$

$$= 166.58.$$

Thus, 167 clusters should be sampled.

The approximate sample size required to estimate τ, using $M\bar{y}$, with a bound, B, on the error of estimation:

$$n = \frac{N\sigma_c^2}{ND + \sigma_c^2}, \qquad\qquad (7.14)$$

where σ_c^2 is estimated by s_c^2 and

$$D = \frac{B^2}{4N^2}.$$

Example 7.7

Again using the data in Table 7.1 as a preliminary sample of incomes in the city, how large a sample is necessary to estimate the total income of all adult males, τ, with a bound of \$1,000,000 on the error of estimation? There are 2500 adult males in the city ($M = 2500$).

Solution

We use equation (7.14) and estimate σ_c^2 by

$$s_c^2 = 634{,}479{,}260$$

as in Example 7.6. When estimating τ,

$$D = \frac{B^2}{4N^2} = \frac{(1{,}000{,}000)^2}{4(415)^2},$$

and

$$ND = \frac{(1,000,000)^2}{4(415)} = 602,409,000.$$

Then using equation (7.14),

$$n = \frac{N\sigma_c^2}{ND + \sigma_c^2}$$

$$n = \frac{415(634,479,260)}{602,409,000 + 634,479,260}$$

$$= 212.88.$$

Thus, 213 clusters should be sampled to estimate the total income with a bound of $1,000,000 on the error of estimation.

The estimator $N\bar{y}_t$, shown in equation (7.8), is used to estimate τ when M is unknown. The estimated variance of $N\bar{y}_t$, shown in equation (7.9), is

$$\hat{V}(N\bar{y}_t) = N^2\left(\frac{N-n}{Nn}\right)s_t^2,$$

where

$$s_t^2 = \frac{\sum\limits_{i=1}^{n}(y_i - \bar{y}_t)^2}{n-1}. \qquad (7.15)$$

Thus, the population variance of $N\bar{y}_t$ is

$$V(N\bar{y}_t) = N^2 V(\bar{y}_t) = N^2\left(\frac{N-n}{Nn}\right)\sigma_t^2, \qquad (7.16)$$

where σ_t^2 is the population quantity estimated by s_t^2.

Estimation of τ with a bound of B units on the error of estimation leads to the following equation:

$$2\sqrt{V(N\bar{y}_t)} = B.$$

Using equation (7.16), one can solve for n.

The approximate sample size required to estimate τ, using $N\bar{y}_t$, with a bound, B, on the error of estimation:

$$n = \frac{N\sigma_t^2}{ND + \sigma_t^2},\qquad (7.17)$$

where σ_t^2 is estimated by s_t^2, and

$$D = \frac{B^2}{4N^2}.$$

Example 7.8

Assume the data of Table 7.1 are from a preliminary study of incomes in the city and M is not known. Then how large a sample must be taken to estimate the total income of all adult males, τ, with a bound of $1,000,000 on the error of estimation?

Solution

The quantity σ_t^2 must be estimated by s_t^2 which is calculated from the data of Table 7.1. Using the calculations of Example 7.4,

$$s_t^2 = \frac{\sum_{i=1}^{n}(y_i - \bar{y}_t)^2}{n-1} = \frac{11,389,360,000}{24}$$

$$= 474,556,667.$$

The bound on the error of estimation is $B = 1,000,000$, and hence,

$$D = \frac{B^2}{4N^2} = \frac{(1,000,000)^2}{4(415)^2}.$$

From equation (7.17),

$$n = \frac{N\sigma_t^2}{ND + \sigma_t^2}$$

$$= \frac{415(474,556,667)}{\dfrac{(415)(1,000,000)^2}{4(415)^2} + 474,556,667}$$

$$= 182.88.$$

Thus, a sample of 183 clusters must be taken to have a bound of $1,000,000 on the error of estimation.

7.5   Estimation of a Population Proportion

Suppose an experimenter wishes to estimate a population proportion, or fraction, such as the proportion of houses in a state with inadequate plumbing or the proportion of corporation presidents who are college graduates. The best estimator of the population proportion, p, is the sample proportion, $\hat{p}$. Let a_i denote the total number of elements in cluster i that possess the characteristic of interest. Then the proportion of elements in the sample of n clusters possessing the characteristic is given by

$$\hat{p} = \frac{\sum_{i=1}^{n} a_i}{\sum_{i=1}^{n} m_i},$$

where m_i is the number of elements in the ith cluster, $i = 1, \ldots, n$. Note that $\hat{p}$ has the same form as $\bar{y}$ (see equation (7.1)), except that y_i is replaced by a_i. The estimated variance of $\hat{p}$ is similar to that of $\bar{y}$.

Estimator of the population proportion p:

$$\hat{p} = \frac{\sum_{i=1}^{n} a_i}{\sum_{i=1}^{n} m_i}. \qquad (7.18)$$

Estimated variance of $\hat{p}$:

$$\hat{V}(\hat{p}) = \frac{N - n}{(Nn\overline{M}^2)} \frac{\sum_{i=1}^{n} (a_i - \hat{p}m_i)^2}{n - 1}. \qquad (7.19)$$

Bound on the error of estimation:

$$2\sqrt{\hat{V}(\hat{p})} = 2\sqrt{\frac{N - n}{(Nn\overline{M}^2)} \frac{\sum_{i=1}^{n} (a_i - \hat{p}m_i)^2}{n - 1}}. \qquad (7.20)$$

The variance formula (7.19) is a good estimator only when the sample size, n, is large, say $n \geq 20$. If $m_1 = m_2 = \cdots = m_N$, then $\hat{p}$ is an unbiased estimator of p, and $\hat{V}(\hat{p})$, shown in equation (7.19), is an unbiased estimator of the actual variance of $\hat{p}$ for any sample size.

Example 7.9

In addition to the information on income, the adult males in the sample survey of Example 7.2 are asked whether they rent or own their homes. The results are given in Table 7.2. Use the data in Table 7.2 to estimate the proportion of adult males in the city who rent their homes. Place a bound on the error of estimation.

Table 7.2   Number of adult males who rent homes.

Cluster	Number of adult males m_i	Number of renters a_i	Cluster	Number of adult males m_i	Number of renters a_i
1	8	4	14	10	5
2	12	7	15	9	4
3	4	1	16	3	1
4	5	3	17	6	4
5	6	3	18	5	2
6	6	4	19	5	3
7	7	4	20	4	1
8	5	2	21	6	3
9	8	3	22	8	3
10	3	2	23	7	4
11	2	1	24	3	0
12	6	3	25	8	3
13	5	2		$\sum_{i=1}^{25} m_i = 151$	$\sum_{i=1}^{25} a_i = 72$

$$\sum_{i=1}^{25} a_i^2 = 262, \qquad \sum_{i=1}^{25} m_i^2 = 1047, \qquad \sum_{i=1}^{25} a_i m_i = 511.$$

Solution

The best estimate of the population proportion of renters is $\hat{p}$, shown in equation (7.18), where

$$\hat{p} = \frac{\sum_{i=1}^{n} a_i}{\sum_{i=1}^{n} m_i} = \frac{72}{151} = .477.$$

To estimate the variance of $\hat{p}$, we must calculate

$$\sum_{i=1}^{n} (a_i - \hat{p}m_i)^2 = \sum_{i=1}^{n} a_i^2 - 2\hat{p} \sum_{i=1}^{n} a_i m_i + \hat{p}^2 \sum_{i=1}^{n} m_i^2$$

and, from Table 7.2,

$$\sum_{i=1}^{n} (a_i - \hat{p}m_i)^2 = 262 - 2(.477)(511) + (.477)^2(1047)$$

$$= 12.729.$$

$\bar{M}$ is estimated by $\bar{m}$, where

$$\bar{m} = \frac{\sum\limits_{i=1}^{n} m_i}{n} = \frac{151}{25} = 6.04.$$

Then, from (7.19),

$$\hat{V}(\hat{p}) = \frac{N-n}{Nn\bar{M}^2} \frac{\sum\limits_{i=1}^{n} (a_i - \hat{p}m_i)^2}{n-1}$$

$$= \frac{(415 - 25)(12.729)}{415(25)(6.04)^2(24)}$$

$$= .00055.$$

The estimate of p with a bound on the error is

$$\hat{p} \pm 2\sqrt{\hat{V}(\hat{p})},$$

$$.477 \pm 2\sqrt{.00055},$$

or

$$.477 \pm .047.$$

Thus, the best estimate of the proportion of adult males who rent homes is .477. The error of estimation should be less than .047 with probability of approximately .95.

7.6   Selecting the Sample Size for Estimating Proportions

Estimation of the population proportion, p, with a bound of B units on the error of estimation implies that the experimenter wants

$$2\sqrt{V(\hat{p})} = B.$$

This equation can be solved for n, and the solution is similar to equation (7.13). That is,

$$n = \frac{N\sigma_c^2}{ND + \sigma_c^2},$$

where $D = B^2 \bar{M}^2 / 4$, and σ_c^2 is estimated by

$$s_c^2 = \frac{\sum_{i=1}^{n} (a_i - \hat{p}m_i)^2}{n - 1}. \qquad (7.21)$$

Equation (7.21) is equation (7.11) with y_i replaced by a_i and $\bar{y}$ by $\hat{p}$.

Example 7.10

The data in Table 7.2 is out of date. A new study will be conducted in the same city for the purpose of estimating the proportion, p, of adult males who rent their homes. How large a sample should be taken to estimate p with a bound of .04 on the error of estimation?

Solution

The best estimate of σ_c^2 is s_c^2 which is calculated using data from Table 7.2:

$$s_c^2 = \frac{\sum_{i=1}^{n} (a_i - \hat{p}m_i)^2}{n - 1} = \frac{12.729}{24} = .530.$$

$\bar{M}$ is estimated by $\bar{m} = 6.04$. Also, D is approximated by

$$\frac{B^2 \bar{m}^2}{4} = \frac{(.04)^2 (6.04)^2}{4} = .0146.$$

Then,

$$n = \frac{N\sigma_c^2}{ND + \sigma_c^2}$$

$$= \frac{(415)(.530)}{(415)(.0146) + .530}$$

$$= 33.40.$$

Thus, 34 clusters should be sampled to estimate p with a bound of .04 on the error of estimation.

7.7 Summary

This chapter introduces a third sample survey design, cluster sampling. In this design each sampling unit is a group, or cluster, of elements. Cluster sampling may provide maximum information at minimum cost when a frame listing population elements is not available or when the cost of obtaining observations increases with increasing distance between elements.

The estimator of the population mean, μ, is the sample mean, $\bar{y}$, given by equation (7.1). The estimated variance of $\bar{y}$ is given by equation (7.2). Two estimators of the population total, τ, are given with their estimated variances. The estimator $M\bar{y}$ is presented in equation (7.4); it is used when the number of elements, M, in the population is known. $N\bar{y}_t$ (see equation (7.8)) is used when M is unknown.

In Section 7.4 we discuss an appropriate sample size for estimating μ or τ with a specified bound on the error of estimation.

In cluster sampling the estimator of a population proportion, p, is the sample proportion, $\hat{p}$, given by equation (7.18). The estimated variance of $\hat{p}$ is given by equation (7.19). The problem of selecting a sample size for estimating a proportion is similar to the problem for estimating a mean.

References

Cochran, W. G., *Sampling Techniques*, 2d ed., New York: John Wiley and Sons, Inc., 1953.

Hansen, M. H., W. N. Hurwitz, and W. G. Madow, *Sample Survey Methods and Theory*, Vol. 1, New York: John Wiley and Sons, Inc., 1953.

Kish, L., *Survey Sampling*, New York: John Wiley and Sons, Inc., 1965.

Exercises

7.1 A manufacturer of band saws wants to estimate the average repair cost per month for the saws he has sold to certain industries. He cannot obtain a repair cost for each saw, but he can obtain the total amount spent for saw repairs and the number of saws owned by each industry. Thus, he decides to use cluster sampling with each industry as a cluster. The manufacturer selects a simple random sample of $n = 20$ from the $N = 96$ industries which he services. The data on total cost of repairs per industry and number of saws per industry are as follows:

Industry	Number of saws	Total repair cost for past month (dollars)
1	3	50
2	7	110
3	11	230
4	9	140
5	2	60
6	12	280
7	14	240
8	3	45
9	5	60
10	9	230
11	8	140
12	6	130
13	3	70
14	2	50
15	1	10
16	4	60
17	12	280
18	6	150
19	5	110
20	8	120

Estimate the average repair cost per saw for the past month, and place a bound on the error of estimation.

7.2   For the data in Exercise 7.1 estimate the total amount spent by the 96 industries on band saw repairs. Place a bound on the error of estimation.

7.3   After checking his sales records, the manufacturer of Exercise 7.1 finds that he sold a total of 710 band saws to these industries. Using this additional information, estimate the total amount spent on saw repairs by these industries and place a bound on the error of estimation.

7.4   The same manufacturer wants to estimate the average repair cost per saw for next month. How many clusters should he select for his sample if he wants the bound on the error of estimation to be less than $2.00?

7.5   A political scientist developed a test designed to measure the degree of awareness of current events. He wants to estimate the average score which would be achieved on this test by all students in a certain high school. The administration at the school would not allow the experimenter to randomly select students out of classes in session, but it would allow him to interrupt a small number of classes for the purpose of giving the test to every member of the class. Thus, the experimenter selects 25 classes at random from the 108 classes in session at a particular hour. The test is given to each member of the sampled classes with the following results:

Class	Number of students	Total score	Class	Number of students	Total score
1	31	1590	14	40	1980
2	29	1510	15	38	1990
3	25	1490	16	28	1420
4	35	1610	17	17	900
5	15	800	18	22	1080
6	31	1720	19	41	2010
7	22	1310	20	32	1740
8	27	1427	21	35	1750
9	25	1290	22	19	890
10	19	860	23	29	1470
11	30	1620	24	18	910
12	18	710	25	31	1740
13	21	1140			

Estimate the average score that would be achieved on this test by all students in the school. Place a bound on the error of estimation.

7.6   The same political scientist of Exercise 7.5 wants to estimate the average test score for a similar high school. If he wants the bound on the error of estimation to be less than 2 points, how many classes should he sample? Assume the school has 100 classes in session during each hour.

7.7   An industry is considering revision of its retirement policy and wants to estimate the proportion of employees which favor the new policy. The industry consists of 87 separate plants located throughout the United States. Since results must be obtained quickly and with little cost, the industry decides to use cluster sampling with each plant as a cluster. A simple random sample of 15 plants is selected, and the opinions of the employees in these plants are obtained by questionnaire. The results are as follows:

Plant	Number of employees	Number favoring new policy	Plant	Number of employees	Number favoring new policy
1	51	42	9	73	54
2	62	53	10	61	45
3	49	40	11	58	51
4	73	45	12	52	29
5	101	63	13	65	46
6	48	31	14	49	37
7	65	38	15	55	42
8	49	30			

Estimate the proportion of employees in the industry who favor the new retirement policy, and place a bound on the error of estimation.

7.8   The industry of Exercise 7.7 modified its retirement policy after obtaining the results of the survey. It now wants to estimate the proportion of employees in favor of the modified policy. How large a sample should be taken to have a bound of .08 on the error of estimation? Use the data from Exercise 7.7 to approximate the results of the new survey.

7.9   An economic survey is designed to estimate the average amount spent on utilities for households in a city. Since no list of households is available, cluster sampling is used with divisions (wards) forming the clusters. A simple random sample of 20 wards is selected from the 60 wards of the city. Interviewers then obtain the cost of utilities from each household within the sampled wards; the total costs are tabulated below.

Sampled ward	Number of households	Total amount spent on utilities	Sampled ward	Number of households	Total amount spent on utilities
1	55	$2210	11	73	$2930
2	60	2390	12	64	2470
3	63	2430	13	69	2830
4	58	2380	14	58	2370
5	71	2760	15	63	2390
6	78	3110	16	75	2870
7	69	2780	17	78	3210
8	58	2370	18	51	2430
9	52	1990	19	67	2730
10	71	2810	20	70	2880

Estimate the average amount a household in the city spends on utilities, and place a bound on the error of estimation.

7.10   In the above survey the number of households in the city is not known. Estimate the total amount spent on utilities for all households in the city, and place a bound on the error of estimation.

7.11   The economic survey of Exercise 7.9 is to be performed in a neighboring city of similar structure. The objective is to estimate the total amount spent on utilities by households in the city with a bound of $5,000 on the error of estimation. Use the data in Exercise 7.9 to find the approximate sample size needed to achieve this bound.

7.12   An inspector wants to estimate the average weight of fill for cereal boxes packaged in a certain factory. The cereal is available to him in cartons containing 12 boxes each. The inspector randomly selects 5 cartons and measures the weight of fill for every box in the sampled cartons, with the following results (in ounces):

Carton						Ounces to fill						
1	16.1	15.9	16.1	16.2	15.9	15.8	16.1	16.2	16.0	15.9	15.8	16.0
2	15.9	16.2	15.8	16.0	16.3	16.1	15.8	15.9	16.0	16.1	16.1	15.9
3	16.2	16.0	15.7	16.3	15.8	16.0	15.9	16.0	16.1	16.0	15.9	16.1
4	15.9	16.1	16.2	16.1	16.1	16.3	15.9	16.1	15.9	15.9	16.0	16.0
5	16.0	15.8	16.3	15.7	16.1	15.9	16.0	16.1	15.8	16.0	16.1	15.9

Estimate the average weight of fill for boxes packaged by this factory, and place a bound on the error of estimation. Assume that the total number of cartons packaged by the factory is large enough for the finite population correction to be ignored.

7.13   A newspaper wants to estimate the proportion of voters favoring a certain candidate, "Candidate A," in a state-wide election. Since it is very expensive to select and interview a simple random sample of registered voters, cluster sampling is used with precincts as clusters. A simple random sample of 50 precincts is selected from the 497 precincts in the state. The newspaper wants to make the estimation on election day, but before final returns are tallied. Therefore, reporters are sent to the polls of each sample precinct to obtain the pertinent information directly from the voters. The results are tabulated below:

No. of voters	Number favoring A	No. of voters	Number favoring A	No. of voters	Number favoring A
1290	680	1893	1143	843	321
1170	631	1942	1187	1066	487
840	475	971	542	1171	596
1620	935	1143	973	1213	782
1381	472	2041	1541	1741	980
1492	820	2530	1679	983	693
1785	933	1567	982	1865	1033
2010	1171	1493	863	1888	987
974	542	1271	742	1947	872
832	457	1873	1010	2021	1093
1247	983	2142	1092	2001	1461
1896	1462	2380	1242	1493	1301
1943	873	1693	973	1783	1167
798	372	1661	652	1461	932
1020	621	1555	523	1237	481
1141	642	1492	831	1843	999
1820	975	1957	932		

Estimate the proportion of voters favoring Candidate A, and place a bound on the error of estimation.

7.14 The same newspaper wants to conduct a similar survey during the next election. How large a sample size will be needed to estimate the proportion of voters favoring a similar candidate with a bound of .05 on the error of estimation? Use the data in Exercise 7.13.

7.15 A forester wishes to estimate the average height of trees on a plantation. The plantation is divided into quarter-acre plots. A simple random sample of 20 plots is selected from the 386 plots on the plantation. All trees on the sampled plots are measured with the following results:

Number of trees	Average height (feet)	Number of trees	Average height (feet)
42	6.2	60	6.3
51	5.8	52	6.7
49	6.7	61	5.9
55	4.9	49	6.1
47	5.2	57	6.0
58	6.9	63	4.9
43	4.3	45	5.3
59	5.2	46	6.7
48	5.7	62	6.1
41	6.1	58	7.0

Estimate the average height of trees on the plantation, and place a bound on the error of estimation. (*Hint:* The total for cluster i can be found by taking m_i times the cluster average.)

7.16   To emphasize safety, a taxi-cab company wants to estimate the proportion of unsafe tires on their 175 cabs. (Ignore spare tires.) It is impractical to select a simple random sample of tires, so cluster sampling is used with each cab as a cluster. A random sample of 25 cabs gives the following number of unsafe tires per cab:

$$2, 4, 0, 1, 2, 0, 4, 1, 3, 1, 2, 0, 1,$$
$$1, 2, 2, 4, 1, 0, 0, 3, 1, 2, 2, 1.$$

Estimate the proportion of unsafe tires being used on the company's cabs, and place a bound on the error of estimation.

8 Systematic Sampling

8.1   Introduction

The final sample survey design discussed in this text is *systematic sampling*.

Definition 8.1   A sample obtained by randomly selecting one element from the first k elements in the frame and every kth element thereafter is called a ***one-in-k systematic sample***.

As in previous chapters, we present methods for estimating a population mean, total, and proportion. We will also discuss appropriate bounds on the error of estimation and sample size requirements.

Systematic sampling provides a useful alternative to simple random sampling for the following reasons:

1. Systematic sampling is easier to perform and hence is less subject to interviewer errors than simple random sampling.
2. Systematic sampling often provides greater information per unit cost than does simple random sampling.

In general, systematic sampling involves random selection of one element from the first k elements and then selection of every kth element thereafter. This procedure is easier to perform and usually less subject to interviewer error than is simple random sampling. For example, it would be difficult to use simple random sampling to select a sample of $n = 50$ shoppers on a city street corner. The interviewer could not determine which shoppers to include in his sample, because he would not know the population size, N, until all shoppers had passed the corner. In contrast, he could take a systematic sample (say one in 20 shoppers) until the required sample size was obtained. This would be an easy procedure for even an inexperienced interviewer to follow.

In addition to being easier to perform and less subject to interviewer error, systematic sampling *frequently* provides more information per unit cost than does simple random sampling. A systematic sample is *frequently* spread more uniformly over the entire population and thus can provide more information about the population than an equivalent amount of data contained in a simple random sample. Consider the following illustration: We wish to select a one-in-5 systematic sample of travel vouchers from a stack of $N = 1,000$ (that is, sample $n = 200$ vouchers) to determine the proportion of vouchers filed incorrectly. A voucher is drawn at random from the first five vouchers (for example #3), and every fifth voucher thereafter is included in the sample.

Voucher	Voucher sampled
1	
2	
3	3
4	
5	
6	
7	
8	8
9	
10	
⋮	⋮
996	
997	
998	998
999	
1000	

Suppose that most of the first 500 vouchers have been correctly filed but, due to a change in clerks, the second 500 have all been incorrectly filed. Simple random sampling could accidentally select a large number (perhaps all) of the 200 vouchers from either the first or the second five hundred vouchers and hence yield a very poor estimate of p. In contrast, systematic sampling would select an equal number of vouchers from each of the two groups and would give a very accurate estimate of the fraction of vouchers incorrectly filed.

Additional examples are discussed in Section 8.3 to illustrate how to choose between systematic and simple random sampling in a given situation.

8.2   How to Draw a Systematic Sample

Although simple random and systematic sampling both provide useful alternatives to one another, the methods of selecting the sample data are different. A simple random sample from a population is selected using a table of random numbers, as noted in Section 4.3. In contrast, various methods are possible in systematic sampling. The investigator can select a 1-in-3, a 1-in-5, or, in general, a 1-in-k systematic sample. For example, a medical investigator is interested in obtaining information about the average number of times 15,000 specialists prescribed a certain drug in the previous year ($N = 15,000$). To obtain a simple random sample of $n = 1600$ specialists, we would use the methods of Section 4.3 and refer to a table of random numbers; however, this would require a great deal of work. Alternatively, we could select one name (specialist) at random from the first $k = 9$ names appearing on the list, and then select every ninth name thereafter until a sample of size 1600 is selected. This is called a 1-*in*-9 *systematic sample.*

Perhaps you wonder how k is chosen in a given situation. If the population size, N, is known, we can determine an approximate sample size, n, for the survey (see Section 8.5) and then choose k to achieve that sample size. There are $N = 15,000$ specialists in the population for the medical survey. Suppose the required sample size is $n = 100$. We must then choose k to be 150 or less. For $k = 150$, we would obtain exactly $n = 100$ observations, while for $k < 150$, the sample size would be greater than 100.

In general, to obtain a systematic sample of n elements from a population of size N, k must be less than or equal to N/n (that is, $k \leq N/n$). Note in the above example that $k \leq 15000/100$; that is, $k \leq 150$.

We cannot accurately choose k when the population size is unknown. We can determine an approximate sample size (n), but we must guess the value of k needed to achieve a sample of size n. If too large a value of k is chosen, the required sample size, n, will not be obtained using a 1-in-k systematic sample from the population. This presents no problem if the experimenter can return to the population and conduct another 1-in-k systematic sample until the required sample size is obtained. However, in some situations it is impossible to start a second systematic sample. For example, it would be impossible to conduct another 1-in-20 systematic sample of shoppers if the required sample of $n = 50$ shoppers is not obtained at the time they pass the corner.

8.3 Estimation of a Population Mean and Total

As we have repeatedly stressed, the objective of most sample surveys is to estimate one or more population parameters. We can estimate a population mean, μ, from a systematic sample using the sample mean, $\bar{y}$. This is shown in equation (8.1).

Estimator of the population mean μ:

$$\hat{\mu} = \bar{y}_{sy} = \frac{\sum_{i=1}^{n} y_i}{n}. \tag{8.1}$$

where the subscript sy signifies that systematic sampling was used.

Estimated variance of $\bar{y}_{st}$:

$$\hat{V}(\bar{y}_{st}) = \left(\frac{N-n}{N}\right)\frac{s^2}{n}. \tag{8.2}$$

Bound on the error of estimation:

$$2\sqrt{\hat{V}(\bar{y}_{sy})} = 2\sqrt{\left(\frac{N-n}{N}\right)\frac{s^2}{n}}. \tag{8.3}$$

If N is unknown, we eliminate the *fpc*, $(N-n)/N$, in equations (8.2) and (8.3).

You will recognize that the estimated variance of $\bar{y}_{st}$ given in equation (8.2) is identical to the estimated variance of $\bar{y}$ obtained using simple random sampling (Section 4.3). This does not imply that the corresponding population variances are equal. The variance of $\bar{y}$ is given by

$$V(\bar{y}) = \frac{\sigma^2}{n}\left(\frac{N-n}{N-1}\right). \tag{8.4}$$

Similarly, it can be shown that the variance of $\bar{y}_{sy}$ is given by

$$V(\bar{y}_{sy}) = \frac{\sigma^2}{n}\{1 + (n-1)\rho\}, \tag{8.5}$$

where ρ is the correlation coefficient between observations in the same systematic sample. When N is large, the two variances are the same if observations within a specified sample are uncorrelated ($\rho \approx 0$).

An unbiased estimate of $V(\bar{y}_{sy})$ cannot be obtained using the data from only one systematic sample. This does not imply that we can never obtain an estimate of $V(\bar{y}_{sy})$. For certain populations systematic sampling is equivalent to simple random sampling, and we can take $V(\bar{y}_{sy})$ to be approximately equal to the estimated variance of $\bar{y}$ based on simple random sampling.

For which populations does this relationship occur? To answer this question, we must consider the following three types of populations:

1. Random population.
2. Ordered population
3. Periodic population.

Definition 8.2   A population is ***random*** if the elements of the population are in random order.

Elements of a systematic sample drawn from a random population are expected to be heterogeneous with ρ approximately equal to zero. Thus, when N is large, the variance of $\bar{y}_{sy}$ is approximately equal to the variance of $\bar{y}$ based on simple random sampling. Systematic sampling in this case is equivalent to simple random sampling. For example, an investigator wishes to determine the average number of prescriptions written by certain doctors during the previous year. If the frame consists of a current alphabetical listing of doctors, it is reasonable to assume that the names on the list are unrelated to the number of prescriptions written for a particular drug. Hence, we consider the population random. A systematic sample would be equivalent to a simple random sample in this case.

Definition 8.3   A population is ***ordered*** if the elements within the population are ordered in magnitude according to some scheme.

In a survey to estimate the effectiveness of instruction in a large introductory course, students are asked to evaluate their instructor according to a numerical scale. A sample is then drawn from a list of evaluations which are arranged in ascending numerical order. The population of measurements from which the sample is drawn is considered an *ordered* population.

A systematic sample drawn from an ordered population is generally heter-ogenous with $\rho \leq 0$. It can be shown using equations (8.4) and (8.5) that when N is large and $\rho \leq 0$,

$$V(\bar{y}_{sy}) \leq V(\bar{y}).$$

Thus, a systematic sample from an ordered population provides more infor-mation per unit cost than does a simple random sample, because the variance of $\bar{y}_{sy}$ is less than the corresponding variance of $\bar{y}$.

Since we cannot obtain an estimate of $V(\bar{y}_{sy})$ from the sample data, a conser-vative estimate (one that is larger than we would expect) of $V(\bar{y}_{sy})$ is given by

$$\hat{V}(\bar{y}_{sy}) = \frac{s^2}{n}\left(\frac{N-n}{N}\right).$$

Definition 8.4   A population is **periodic** if the elements of the population have cyclical variation.

Suppose we are interested in determining the average daily sales volume for a chain of grocery stores. The population of daily sales is clearly periodic with peak sales occurring towards the end of each week. The effectiveness of a 1-in-k sample depends upon the value we choose for k. If we sample daily sales every Wednesday, we would probably underestimate the true average daily sales volume. Similarly, if we sample sales every Friday, we would probably over-estimate the true average sales. We might sample every ninth workday to avoid consistently sampling either the low or high sales days.

Elements of a systematic sample drawn from a periodic population can be homogeneous (that is, $\rho > 0$). For example, the elements within a systematic sample of daily sales taken every Wednesday would be fairly homogeneous. It can be shown, using equations (8.4) and (8.5), that when N is large and $\rho > 0$,

$$V(\bar{y}_{sy}) > V(\bar{y}).$$

Thus, in this case systematic sampling provides less information per unit cost than does simple random sampling. As in the preceding situations, $V(\bar{y}_{sy})$ cannot be estimated directly using a single systematic sample. We can approximate its value using $\hat{V}(\bar{y})$ as for simple random sampling. In general this should under-estimate the true variance of $\bar{y}_{sy}$.

To avoid this problem which occurs with systematic sampling from a periodic population, the investigator could change the random starting point several times. This would reduce the possibility of choosing observations from the same relative position in a periodic population. For example, when a 1-in-10 system-atic sample is being drawn from a long list of file cards, a card is randomly selected from the first 10 cards (for example, number 2) and every tenth card thereafter. This procedure can be altered by randomly selecting a card from the first 10 (for example, number 2) and every tenth card thereafter for perhaps 15 selections to obtain the numbers

$$2, 12, 22, \ldots, 152.$$

At this point, another random starting point can be selected from the next 10 numbers

$$153, 154, 155, \ldots, 162.$$

If 156 is selected, we then proceed to select every 10th number thereafter for the next 15 selections. This entire process would be repeated until the desired sample size is obtained.

The process of selecting a random starting point several times throughout the systematic sample has the effect of shuffling the elements of the population and then drawing a systematic sample. Hence, we can assume that the sample obtained is equivalent to a systematic sample drawn from a random population. The variance of $\bar{y}_{sy}$ can then be approximated using

$$\hat{V}(\bar{y}_{sy}) = \frac{s^2}{n}\left(\frac{N-n}{N}\right).$$

Example 8.1

An investigator wishes to determine the quality of maple syrup contained in the sap of trees on a Vermont farm. The total number of trees, N, is unknown; hence, it is impossible to conduct a simple random sample of trees. As an alternative procedure, the investigator decides to use a 1-in-7 systematic sample. The data from this survey are listed below. Entries are the percentage of sugar content (in the sap) for the trees sampled. Use these data to estimate μ, the average sugar content of maple trees on the farm. Place a bound on the error of estimation.

Tree sampled	Sugar content of the sap y	y^2
1	82	6724
2	76	5776
3	83	6889
$\vdots$	$\vdots$	$\vdots$
210	84	7056
211	80	6400
212	79	6241
	$\sum_{i=1}^{212} y_i = 17{,}066$	$\sum_{i=1}^{212} y_i^2 = 1{,}486{,}800$

Solution

An estimate of μ is given by

$$\bar{y}_{sy} = \frac{\sum\limits_{i=1}^{n} y_i}{n} = \frac{17{,}066}{212} = 80.5.$$

To find a bound on the error of estimation we must first compute s^2. Using the computational formula,

$$s^2 = \frac{\sum y_i^2 - \dfrac{(\sum y_i)^2}{n}}{n-1}$$

$$= \frac{1{,}486{,}800 - \dfrac{(17{,}066)^2}{212}}{211}$$

$$= 535.483.$$

Intuitively, it is reasonable to assume that the population of trees on the farm is random. Under this assumption, the estimated variance of $\bar{y}_{sy}$ is given by equation (8.2). Having conducted the 1-in-7 sample, we know N. Assuming $N = 1484$,

$$\hat{V}(\bar{y}_{sy}) = \frac{s^2}{n}\left(\frac{N-n}{N}\right)$$

$$= \frac{535.483}{212}\left(\frac{1484-212}{1484}\right) = 2.165.$$

An approximate bound on the error of estimation is given by

$$2\sqrt{\hat{V}(\bar{y}_{sy})} \approx 2\sqrt{2.165} = 2.942.$$

To summarize, we estimate the average sugar content of the sap to be 80.5 percent. We are quite confident that the bound on the error of estimation is less than 2.942%.

The reader will recall that estimation of a population total requires knowledge of the total number of elements, N, in the population when using the procedures of Chapters 4, 5 and 7. For example, we use

$$\hat{\tau} = N\bar{y}$$

as an estimator of τ based on simple random sampling. Also, we use

$$\hat{\tau}_{st} = \sum_{i=1}^{L} N_i \, \bar{y}_i \, ,$$

where

$$\sum_{i=1}^{L} N_i = N,$$

as an estimator of τ based on stratified random sampling from L strata (Section 5.3). Similarly, we need to know N to estimate τ using systematic sampling.

The population size is unknown in many practical situations which suggest using systematic sampling; however, when N is known, we can estimate τ using equations (8.6), (8.7), and (8.8).

Estimator of the population total τ:

$$\hat{\tau} = N\bar{y}_{sy} . \qquad (8.6)$$

Estimated variance of $\hat{\tau}$:

$$\hat{V}(N\bar{y}_{sy}) = N^2 \hat{V}(\bar{y}_{sy}) = N^2 \left\{ \frac{s^2}{n} \left(\frac{N-n}{N} \right) \right\}. \qquad (8.7)$$

Bound on the error of estimation:

$$2\sqrt{\hat{V}(N\bar{y}_{sy})} = 2\sqrt{N^2 \left\{ \frac{s^2}{n} \left(\frac{N-n}{N} \right) \right\}}. \qquad (8.8)$$

Note that the results presented in equations (8.6), (8.7), and (8.8) are identical to those presented for estimating a population total under simple random sampling. This does not imply that the variance of $N\bar{y}_{sy}$ is the same as the variance of $N\bar{y}$. Again, we cannot obtain an unbiased estimator of $V(N\bar{y}_{sy})$ from the data in a single systematic sample. However, in certain circumstances, as noted earlier, systematic sampling is equivalent to simple random sampling, and we can use the results presented in Section 4.3.

Example 8.2

A Virginia horticulturist has an experimental orchard of $N = 1300$ apple trees of a new variety under study. The investigator wishes to estimate the total yield (in bushels) from the orchard, based on a 1-in-10 systematic sample of trees. The sample mean and variance for the sampled trees are found to be $\bar{y}_{sy} = 3.52$ bushels and $s^2 = .48$ bushels, respectively. Use these data to estimate τ, and place a bound on the error of estimation.

Solution

It seems reasonable to assume that the population is random; hence, systematic and simple random sampling are equivalent. If the population were periodic, the experimenter could choose several random starting points in selecting the trees to be included in the sample.

An estimate of τ is given by

$$\hat{\tau} = N\bar{y}_{sy} = 1300(3.52) = 4576.$$

A bound on the error of estimation can be found using equation (8.8) with $n = 130$.

$$2\sqrt{\hat{V}(N\bar{y}_{sy})} = 2\sqrt{N^2 \left\{ \frac{s^2}{n}\left(\frac{N-n}{N} \right) \right\}}$$

$$= 2\sqrt{1300^2 \left\{ \frac{.48}{130}\left(\frac{1300-130}{1300} \right) \right\}}$$

$$= 149.88.$$

Thus, we estimate that the total yield from the apple orchard is 4575 bushels with a bound on the error of estimation of 149.88 bushels.

8.4   Estimation of a Population Proportion

An investigator frequently wishes to use data from a systematic sample to estimate a population proportion. For example, to determine the proportion of registered voters in favor of an upcoming bond issue, it would be convenient to use a 1-in-k systematic sample from the voter registration list.

The estimator of the population proportion, p, obtained from systematic sampling is denoted by $\hat{p}_{sy}$. As in simple random sampling (Section 4.5), the properties of $\hat{p}_{sy}$ parallel those of the sample mean, $\bar{y}_{sy}$, if the response measurements are defined as follows: let $y_i = 0$ if the ith element sampled does not possess the specified characteristic and $y_i = 1$ if it does. The estimator, $\hat{p}_{sy}$, is then the average of the 0 and 1 values from the sample.

Estimator of the population proportion p:

$$\hat{p}_{sy} = \bar{y}_{sy} = \frac{\sum\limits_{i=1}^{n} y_i}{n}. \tag{8.9}$$

Estimated variance of $\hat{p}_{sy}$:

$$\hat{V}(\hat{p}_{sy}) = \frac{\hat{p}_{sy}\hat{q}_{sy}}{n-1}\left(\frac{N-n}{N}\right), \tag{8.10}$$

where $\hat{q}_{sy} = 1 - \hat{p}_{sy}$.

Bound on the error of estimation:

$$2\sqrt{\hat{V}(\hat{p}_{sy})} = 2\sqrt{\frac{\hat{p}_{sy}\hat{q}_{sy}}{n-1}\left(\frac{N-n}{N}\right)}. \tag{8.11}$$

We can ignore the *fpc*, $(N-n)/N$, in equations (8.10) and (8.11) if the population size, N, is unknown.

We again note that the estimated variance of $\hat{p}_{sy}$ (or $\bar{y}_{sy}$) is identical to the estimated variance of $\hat{p}$ (or $\bar{y}$) using simple random sampling (Section 4.5). This does not imply that the corresponding population variances are equal; however, if N is large, and if the observations within a systematic sample are unrelated (that is, $\rho = 0$), the two population variances will be equal.

Example 8.3

A 1-in-6 systematic sample is obtained from a voter registration list to estimate the proportion of voters in favor of the proposed bond issue. Several different random starting points are used to insure that the results of the sample are not affected by periodic variation in the population. The coded results of this pre-election survey are as follows:

Voter	Response
4	1
10	0
16	1
$\vdots$	$\vdots$
5760	0
5766	0
5772	1

$$\sum_{i=1}^{962} y_i = 652$$

Estimate p, the proportion of the 5775 registered voters in favor of the proposed bond issue ($N = 5775$). Place a bound on the error of estimation.

Solution

The sample proportion is given by

$$\hat{p}_{sy} = \frac{\sum_{i=1}^{962} y_i}{962} = \frac{652}{962} = .678.$$

Since N is large and several random starting points were chosen in drawing the systematic sample, we can assume that

$$\hat{V}(\hat{p}_{sy}) = \frac{\hat{p}_{sy}\hat{q}_{sy}}{n-1}\left(\frac{N-n}{N}\right)$$

provides a good estimate of $V(\hat{p}_{sy})$.
    The bound on the error of estimation is

$$2\sqrt{\hat{V}(\hat{p}_{sy})} = 2\sqrt{\frac{\hat{p}_{sy}\hat{q}_{sy}}{n-1}\left(\frac{N-n}{N}\right)}$$

$$= 2\sqrt{\frac{(.678)(.322)}{961}\left(\frac{5775-962}{5775}\right)}$$

$$\approx .0275.$$

Thus, we estimate .678 (67.8%) of the registered voters favor the proposed bond issue. We are relatively confident that the error of estimation is less than .0275 (2.75%).

8.5   Selecting the Sample Size

Now let us determine the number of observations necessary to estimate μ to within B units. The required sample size is found by solving the following equation for n:

$$2\sqrt{V(\bar{y}_{sy})} = B. \qquad (8.12)$$

The solution to equation (8.12) involves both σ^2 and ρ which must be known (at least approximately) in order to solve for n. Although these parameters sometimes can be estimated if data from a prior survey are available we do not discuss this method in text. Instead we use the formula for n based on simple random sampling. This formula could give an extra large sample for ordered populations and too small a sample for periodic populations. As noted earlier, the variances of $\bar{y}_{sy}$ and $\bar{y}$ are equivalent if the population is random.

The sample size required to estimate μ with a bound, B, on the error of estimation:

$$n = \frac{N\sigma^2}{(N-1)D + \sigma^2}, \qquad (8.13)$$

where

$$D = \frac{B^2}{4}.$$

Example 8.4

The management of a large utility company is interested in the average amount of time delinquent bills are overdue. A systematic sample will be drawn from an alphabetical list of $N = 2500$ overdue customer accounts. In a similar survey conducted the previous year, the sample variance was found to be $s^2 = 100$ days. Determine the sample size required to estimate μ, the average amount of time utility bills are overdue, with a bound on the error of estimation of $B = 2$ days.

Solution

It is reasonable to assume that the population of interest is random; hence $\rho \approx 0$. Then we can use equation (8.13) to find the approximate sample size. Replacing σ^2 by s^2 and setting

$$D = \frac{B^2}{4} = \frac{4}{4} = 1,$$

we have

$$n = \frac{N\sigma^2}{(N-1)D + \sigma^2} = \frac{2500(100)}{2499(1) + 100} = 96.19.$$

Thus, management must sample approximately 97 accounts to estimate the average amount of time delinquent bills are overdue, to within two days.

To determine the sample size required to estimate τ with a bound on the error of estimation of magnitude B, we use the corresponding method presented in Section 4.4.

The sample size required to estimate p to within B units is found using the sample size formula for estimating p under simple random sampling.

Sample size required to estimate p with a bound, B, on the error of estimation:

$$n = \frac{Npq}{(N-1)D + pq},\tag{8.14}$$

where

$$q = 1 - p \text{ and } D = \frac{B^2}{4}.$$

In a practical situation we do not know p. We can find an approximate sample size by replacing p with an estimated value. If no prior information is available to estimate p, we can obtain a conservative sample size by setting $p = .5$.

Example 8.5

An advertising firm is starting a promotion campaign for a new product. The firm wants to sample potential customers in a small community to determine customer acceptance.

To eliminate some of the costs associated with personal interviews, the investigators decide to run a systematic sample from $N = 5000$ names listed in a community registry and collect the data via telephone interviews. Determine the sample size required to estimate p, the proportion of people who consider the product "acceptable," with a bound on the error of estimation of magnitude $B = .03$ (that is, 3%).

Solution

The required sample size can be found by using equation (8.14). Although no previous data are available on this new product, we can still find an approximate sample size. Set $p = .5$ in equation (8.14) and

$$D = \frac{B^2}{4} = \frac{(.03)^2}{4} = .00022.$$

Then the required sample size is

$$n = \frac{Npq}{(N-1)D + pq}$$

$$= \frac{5000(.5)(.5)}{4999(.000225) + (.5)(.5)}$$

$$= 909.240.$$

Hence, the firm must interview 910 people to determine consumer acceptance to within 3%.

8.6   Repeated Systematic Sampling

We state in Section 8.3 that it is impossible to estimate the variance of $\bar{y}_{sy}$ based on information contained in a single systematic sample unless the systematic sampling generates, for all practical purposes, a random sample. When this occurs we can use the random sampling estimation procedures outlined in Section 4.3. However, in most cases systematic random sampling is not equivalent to simple random sampling. An alternate method must be used to estimate $V(\bar{y}_{sy})$. Repeated systematic sampling is one such method.

As the name implies, repeated systematic sampling requires the selection of more than one systematic sample. For example, ten 1-in-50 systematic samples, each containing six measurements, could be acquired in approximately the same time as a 1-in-5 systematic sample containing 60 measurements. Both procedures yield 60 measurements for estimating the population mean, μ, but the repeated sampling procedure allows us to estimate $V(\bar{y}_{sy})$ using the square of the deviations of the $n_s = 10$ individual sample means about their mean. The average, $\hat{\mu}$, of the 10 sample means will estimate the population mean, μ.

To select n_s repeated systematic samples, we must space the elements of each sample further apart. Thus, ten 1-in-50 samples ($n_s = 10$, $k' = 50$) of six measurements each contains the same number of measurements as does a single 1-in-5 sample ($k = 5$) containing $n = 60$ measurements. The starting point for each of the n_s systematic samples is randomly selected from the first k' elements. The remaining elements in each sample are acquired by adding k', $2k'$, and so forth, to the starting point until the total number per sample, n/n_s, is obtained.

A population consists of $N = 960$ elements which we can number consecutively. To select a systematic sample of size $n = 60$, we choose $k = N/n = 16$ and a random number between 1 and 16 as a starting point. What procedure do we follow to select 10 repeated systematic samples in place of the one systematic sample? First, we choose $k' = 10k = 10(16) = 160$. Next, we select ten random numbers between 1 and 160. Finally, the constant 160 is added to each of these random starting points to obtain ten numbers between 161 and 320; the process of adding the constant is continued until ten samples of size 6 are obtained.
    A random selection of ten integers between 1 and 160 gives the following:

$$73, 42, 81, 145, 6, 21, 86, 17, 112, 102.$$

These numbers form the random starting points for ten systematic samples, as shown in Table 8.1. The second element in each sample is found by adding 160 to the first, the third by adding 160 to the second, and so forth.

Table 8.1   Selection of repeated systematic samples.

Random starting point	Second element in sample	Third element in sample		Sixth element in sample
6	166	326	$\cdots$	806
17	177	337	$\cdots$	817
21	181	341	$\cdots$	821
42	202	362	$\cdots$	842
73	233	393	$\cdots$	873
81	241	401	$\cdots$	881
86	246	406	$\cdots$	886
102	262	422	$\cdots$	902
112	272	432	$\cdots$	912
145	305	465	$\cdots$	945

We frequently select $n_s = 10$ to allow us to obtain enough sample means to acquire a satisfactory estimate of $V(\hat{\mu})$. We choose k' to give the same number of measurements as would be obtained in a single 1-in-k systematic sample; thus,

$$k' = kn_s.$$

The formulas for estimating μ from n_s systematic samples are shown in equations (8.15), (8.16), and (8.17).

Estimator of the population mean, μ, using n_s one-in-k' systematic samples:

$$\hat{\mu} = \sum_{i=1}^{n_s} \frac{\bar{y}_i}{n_s}, \qquad (8.15)$$

where $\bar{y}_i$ represents the average of the ith systematic sample.

Estimated variance of $\hat{\mu}$:

$$\hat{V}(\hat{\mu}) = \left(\frac{N-n}{N}\right) \frac{\sum_{i=1}^{n_s} (\bar{y}_i - \hat{\mu})^2}{n_s(n_s - 1)}. \qquad (8.16)$$

Bound on the error of estimation:

$$2\sqrt{\hat{V}(\hat{\mu})} = 2\sqrt{\left(\frac{N-n}{N}\right) \frac{\sum_{i=1}^{n_s} (\bar{y}_i - \hat{\mu})^2}{n_s(n_s - 1)}}. \qquad (8.17)$$

We can also use repeated systematic sampling to estimate a population total, τ, if N is known. The necessary formulas are given in equations (8.18), (8.19), and (8.20).

Estimator of the population total, τ, using n_s one-in-k' systematic samples:

$$\hat{\tau} = N\hat{\mu} = N \sum_{i=1}^{n_s} \frac{\bar{y}_i}{n_s}. \qquad (8.18)$$

Estimated variance of $\hat{\tau}$:

$$\hat{V}(\hat{\tau}) = N^2 \hat{V}(\hat{\mu}) = N^2 \left(\frac{N-n}{N}\right) \frac{\sum_{i=1}^{n_s} (\bar{y}_i - \hat{\mu})^2}{n_s(n_s - 1)}. \qquad (8.19)$$

Bound on the error of estimation:

$$2\hat{V}(\hat{\tau}) = 2\sqrt{N^2 \left(\frac{N-n}{N}\right) \frac{\sum_{i=1}^{n_s} (\bar{y}_i - \hat{\mu})^2}{n_s(n_s - 1)}}. \qquad (8.20)$$

Example 8.6

A state park charges admission by carload rather than by person, and a park official wants to estimate the average number of persons per car for a particular summer holiday. He knows from past experience that there should be about 400 cars entering the park, and he wants to sample 80 cars. To obtain an estimate of the variance, he uses repeated systematic sampling with 10 samples of 8 cars each. Using the data given below, estimate the average number of persons per car and place a bound on the error of estimation.

Solution

For one systematic sample,

$$k = \frac{N}{n} = \frac{400}{80} = 5;$$

hence, for $n_s = 10$ samples,

$$k' = 10k = 10(5) = 50.$$

The following ten random numbers between 1 and 50 are drawn:

$$13, 35, 2, 40, 26, 7, 31, 45, 5, 46.$$

Cars with these numbers form the random starting points for the systematic samples.

Table 8.2   Data on number of persons per car. (The responses, y_i, are in parentheses.)

Random starting point	Second element	Third element	Fourth element	Fifth element	Sixth element	Seventh element	Eighth element	$\bar{y}_i$
2 (3)	52 (4)	102 (5)	152 (3)	202 (6)	252 (1)	302 (4)	352 (4)	3.75
5 (5)	55 (3)	105 (4)	155 (2)	205 (4)	255 (2)	305 (3)	355 (4)	3.38
7 (2)	57 (4)	107 (6)	157 (2)	207 (3)	257 (2)	307 (1)	357 (3)	2.88
13 (6)	63 (4)	113 (6)	163 (7)	213 (2)	263 (3)	313 (2)	363 (7)	4.62
26 (4)	76 (5)	126 (7)	176 (4)	226 (2)	276 (6)	326 (2)	376 (6)	4.50
31 (7)	81 (6)	131 (4)	181 (4)	231 (3)	281 (6)	331 (7)	381 (5)	5.25
35 (3)	85 (3)	135 (2)	185 (3)	235 (6)	285 (5)	335 (6)	385 (8)	4.50
40 (2)	90 (6)	140 (2)	190 (5)	240 (5)	290 (4)	340 (4)	390 (5)	4.12
45 (2)	95 (6)	145 (3)	195 (6)	245 (4)	295 (4)	345 (5)	395 (4)	4.25
46 (6)	96 (5)	146 (4)	196 (6)	246 (3)	296 (3)	346 (5)	396 (3)	4.38

The quantity $\bar{y}_1$ is the average for the first row, $\bar{y}_2$ the average for the second row, and so forth.

The estimate of μ is

$$\hat{\mu} = \frac{1}{n_s} \sum_{i=1}^{n_s} \bar{y}_i = \frac{1}{10} (3.75 + 3.38 + \cdots + 4.38)$$

$$= 4.163.$$

The following identity is easily established:

$$\sum_{i=1}^{n_s} (\bar{y}_i - \hat{\mu})^2 = \sum_{i=1}^{n_s} \bar{y}_i^2 - \frac{1}{n_s} \left(\sum_{i=1}^{n_s} \bar{y}_i \right)^2.$$

Substituting, we obtain

$$\sum_{i=1}^{10} (\bar{y}_i - \hat{\mu})^2 = 177.410 - \frac{1}{10} (1733.06)$$

$$= 4.104.$$

Thus, the estimated variance of $\hat{\mu}$ becomes

$$\hat{V}(\hat{\mu}) = \left(\frac{N-n}{N} \right) \frac{\sum_{i=1}^{n_s} (\bar{y}_i - \hat{\mu})^2}{n_s(n_s - 1)}$$

$$= \left(\frac{400 - 80}{400} \right) \frac{(4.104)}{10(9)} = .0365.$$

The estimate of μ with a bound on the error of estimation is

$$\hat{\mu} \pm 2\sqrt{\hat{V}(\hat{\mu})},$$

$$4.163 \pm 2\sqrt{.0365},$$

or

$$4.163 \pm .382.$$

Therefore, our best estimate of the average number of persons per car is 4.163. The error of estimation should be less than .382 with probability approximately .95.

8.7   Summary

Systematic sampling is the final sample survey design presented in this text. It is presented as an alternative to simple random sampling. Systematic sampling is easier to perform and, therefore, is less subject to interviewer errors than simple random sampling. In addition, systematic sampling often provides more information per unit cost than does simple random sampling.

We consider estimation of a population mean, total, and proportion using the estimators, $\bar{y}_{sy}$, $N\bar{y}_{sy}$, and $\hat{p}_{sy}$, respectively. The corresponding bounds on the errors of estimation are given for these estimators.

One must first consider the type of population under investigation in order to choose between systematic and simple random sampling. For example, when N is large and $\rho < 0$, the variance of $\bar{y}_{sy}$ is smaller than the corresponding variance of $\bar{y}$ based on simple random sampling. A systematic sample is preferable when the population of interest is ordered and N is large. When the population is random, the two sampling procedures are equivalent and either design can be used. Care must be used in applying systematic sampling to periodic populations.

Sample size requirements for estimating μ, τ, and p are determined using formulas presented for simple random sampling.

Repeated systematic sampling is discussed in Section 8.6; it allows the experimenter to estimate the population mean or total and the variance of the estimator without making any assumptions about the nature of the population.

References

Cochran, W. G., *Sampling Techniques*, 2d ed., New York: John Wiley and Sons, Inc., 1953.

Deming, W. E., *Sample Design in Business Research*, New York: John Wiley and Sons, Inc., 1960.

Jones, H. L., "Investigation of the Properties of a Sample Mean by Employing Random Subsample Means," *Journal of the American Statistical Association*, **51**(1956), 54–83.

Kish, L., *Survey Sampling*, New York: John Wiley and Sons, Inc., 1965.

Exercises

8.1   The management of a particular company is interested in estimating the proportion of employees favoring a new investment policy. A one-in-10 systematic sample is obtained from employees leaving the building at the end of a particular workday. Use these data to estimate p, the proportion in favor of the new policy, and place a bound on the error of estimation. Assume $N = 2000$.

Employee sampled	Response
3	1
13	0
23	1
⋮	⋮
1993	1

$$\sum_{i=1}^{200} y_i = 132$$

8.2   Determine the sample size required to estimate p to within .01 units. What type of systematic sample should be run?

8.3   The quality control section of an industrial firm uses systematic sampling to estimate the average amount of fill in 12-ounce cans coming off an assembly line. The data below represent a 1-in-50 systematic sample of the production in one day. Estimate μ and place a bound on the error of estimation. Assume $N = 1800$.

Amount of fill in ounces

12.00	12.03
11.91	11.98
11.87	11.87
12.05	11.93
11.72	11.97
11.85	12.05
11.97	12.01
11.98	12.00
12.01	11.90
11.87	11.94
11.93	11.93
11.98	12.02
12.01	11.80
12.03	11.83
11.98	11.88
11.91	11.89
11.95	12.05
11.87	12.04

8.4   Use the data of Exercise 8.3 to determine the sample size required to estimate μ to within .03 units.

8.5   Soil experts want to determine the amount of exchangeable calcium (in parts per million) in a plot of ground. To simplify the sampling scheme, a rectangular grid is superimposed on the field. Soil samples are taken at each point of intersection on the grid (see picture below).

Use the following data to determine the average amount of exchangeable calcium on the plot of ground. Place a bound on the error of estimation.

$$n = 45,$$

$$\sum y_i = 90,320 \quad \text{exchangeable calcium,}$$

$$\sum y_i^2 = 148,030,000.$$

8.6   The Highway Patrol of a particular state is concerned about the proportion of motorists who carry their licenses. A check point is set up on a major highway and the driver of every seventh car is questioned. Use the data below to estimate the proportion of drivers carrying their licenses. Place a bound on the error of estimation. Assume that $N = 2800$ cars pass the check point during the sampling period.

Car	Response, y_i
1	1
2	1
3	0
⋮	⋮
400	1

$$\sum y_i = 324$$

8.7   If the Highway Patrol expects at least $N = 3000$ cars to pass the checkpoint, determine the sample size required to estimate p to within $B = .015$ units.

8.8   A college is concerned about improving its relations with a neighboring community. A 1-in-150 systematic sample of the $N = 4500$ students listed in the directory is taken to estimate the total amount of money spent on clothing during one quarter of the school year. The results of the sample are listed below. Use these data to estimate τ, and place a bound on the error of estimation.

Student	Amount spent (in dollars)	Student	Amount spent (in dollars)
1	30	16	32
2	22	17	14
3	10	18	29
4	62	19	48
5	28	20	50
6	31	21	9
7	40	22	15
8	29	23	6
9	17	24	93
10	51	25	21
11	29	26	20
12	21	27	13
13	13	28	12
14	15	29	29
15	23	30	38

8.9   What sample size is needed to estimate τ in Exercise 8.8 with a bound on the error of estimation approximately equal to \$10,000? What systematic sampling scheme would you recommend?

8.10   A census is conducted in a particular community. In addition to the usual population information, the surveyors question the occupants of every 20th household to determine how long they have occupied their present home. These results are summarized below.

$$n = 115,$$

$$\sum y_i = 407.1, \quad \text{(years)}$$

$$\sum y_i^2 = 2011.15,$$

$$N = 2300.$$

Use these data to estimate the average amount of time people have lived in their present home. Place a bound on the error of estimation.

8.11   A group of guidance counselors are concerned about the average yearly tuition for out-of-state students in 371 junior colleges. From an alphabetical list of these colleges, a 1-in-7 systematic sample is drawn. Data concerning out-of-state tuition expenses for an academic year (September to June) is obtained for each college sampled. Let y_i be the amount of tuition required for the ith college sampled. Use the data below to estimate μ, and place a bound on the error of estimation.

$$\sum_{i=1}^{53} y_i = \$11,950, \qquad \sum_{i=1}^{53} y_i^2 = \$2,731,037.$$

8.12   Museum officials are interested in the total number of persons who visit their museum during a 180 day period when an expensive antique collection is on display. Since it is too costly to monitor the museum traffic each day, officials decide to obtain these data every 10th day. The information from this 1-in-10 systematic sample is summarized below:

Day	Number of people visiting the museum
3	160
13	350
23	225
⋮	⋮
173	290

$$\sum_{i=1}^{18} y_i = 4868 \quad \text{and} \quad \sum_{i=1}^{18} y_i^2 = 1,321,450.$$

Use these data to estimate τ, the total number of persons visiting the museum during the specified period. Place a bound on the error of estimation.

8.13   Foresters are interested in determining the mean timber volume per acre for 520 one-acre plots ($N = 520$). A 1-in-25 systematic sample is conducted. Using the data presented below, estimate μ, the average timber volume per plot, and place a bound on the error of estimation.

Plot sampled	Volume in board feet	Plot sampled	Volume in board feet
4	7030	279	7540
29	6720	304	6720
54	6850	329	6900
79	7210	354	7200
104	7150	379	7100
129	7370	404	6860
154	7000	429	6800
179	6930	454	7050
204	6570	479	7420
229	6910	504	7090
254	7380		

8.14   The officers of a certain professional society wish to determine the proportion of the membership that favors several proposed revisions in refereeing practices. They conduct a 1-in-10 systematic sample from an alphabetical list of the $N = 650$ registered members. Let $y_i = 1$ if the ith person sampled favors the proposed changes and $y_i = 0$ if he opposes the changes. Use the sample data summarized below to estimate p, the proportion of members in favor of the proposed changes. Place a bound on the error of estimation.

$$\sum_{i=1}^{65} y_i = 48.$$

8.15   In a sociological survey, a 1-in-50 systematic sample is drawn from city tax records to determine the total number of families in the city who rent their homes. Let $y_i = 1$ if the family in the ith household sampled rents and let $y_i = 0$ if the family does not. If there are $N = 15{,}200$ households in the community, use the data below to estimate τ, the total number of families who rent. Place a bound on the error of estimation.

$$\sum_{i=1}^{304} y_i = 88.$$

Hint: If $\hat{p}$ = estimated fraction who rent, then $N\hat{p}$ would be an estimate of the total number who rent. $\hat{V}(N\hat{p}) = N^2 \hat{V}(\hat{p})$.

9 Two-Stage Cluster Sampling

9.1 Introduction

Two-stage cluster sampling is an extension of the concept of cluster sampling. You will recall from the discussion of cluster sampling in Chapter 7 that a cluster is usually a convenient or natural collection of elements, such as blocks of households or cartons of flashbulbs. A cluster often contains too many elements to obtain a measurement on each; or, it contains elements so nearly alike that measurement of only a few elements provides information on an entire cluster. When either situation occurs, the experimenter can select a simple random sample of clusters and then take a simple random sample of elements within each cluster. The result is a two-stage cluster sample.

Definition 9.1   A *two-stage cluster sample* is obtained by first selecting a simple random sample of clusters and then selecting a simple random sample of elements from each sampled cluster.

For example, a national survey of university student opinions could be conducted by selecting a simple random sample of universities from all those in the country and then selecting a simple random sample of students from each university. Thus, a university would correspond to a cluster of students. Similarly, the total amount of accounts receivable for a chain store could be estimated by first taking a simple random sample of stores and then selecting a simple random sample of accounts from each. Thus, each chain store provides a cluster of accounts.

Notice the similarity between two-stage cluster sampling and stratified random sampling, where clusters are analogous to strata. The difference is that clusters are sampled from a large body of clusters whose totality is equivalent to the population, whereas strata are often obtained by subdividing the population and *all* strata are included in the sample. Cluster sampling guarantees a sample of elements from only those clusters selected in the random sample, while stratified random sampling guarantees a sample from every stratum in the population.

The advantages of two-stage cluster sampling over other designs are the same as those listed in Chapter 7 for cluster sampling. First, a frame listing all elements in the population may be impossible or costly to obtain, whereas it may be easy to obtain a list of all clusters. For example, it would be expensive and time consuming to compile a list of all university students in the country, but a list of universities could be readily acquired. Second, the cost of obtaining data may be inflated by travel costs if the sampled elements are spread over a large geographic area. Thus, it is often economical to sample clusters of elements which are physically close together.

9.2   How to Draw a Two-Stage Cluster Sample

The first problem in selecting a two-stage cluster sample is the choice of appropriate clusters. Two conditions are desirable: (1) geographic proximity of the elements within a cluster and (2) cluster sizes which are convenient to administer.

The selection of appropriate clusters also depends upon whether we want to sample a few clusters and many elements from each or many clusters and a few elements from each. Ultimately the choice is based on costs. Large clusters tend to possess heterogeneous elements and, hence, a large sample is required from each in order to acquire accurate estimates of population parameters. In contrast, small clusters frequently contain relatively homogeneous elements, in which case accurate information on the characteristics of a cluster can be obtained by selecting a small sample from each cluster.

Consider the problem of sampling personal incomes in a large city. The city could be divided into large clusters, for example precincts, which contain a heterogeneous assortment of incomes. Thus, a small number of precincts might yield a representative cross section of incomes within the city, but a fairly large sample of elements from each cluster would be required in order to accurately estimate its mean (due to the heterogeneity of incomes within the cluster). In contrast, the city could be divided into small, relatively homogeneous clusters, say city blocks. Then a small sample of people from each block would give adequate information on each cluster's mean, but it would require many blocks to obtain accurate information on the mean income for the entire city.

For another example, consider the university student opinion poll. If students within a university hold similar opinions on the question of interest but opinions differ widely from university to university, then the sample should contain a few representatives from many different universities. If the opinions vary greatly within each university, then the survey should include many representatives from each of a few universities.

To select the sample, we first obtain a frame listing all clusters in the population. We then draw a simple random sample of clusters using the random sampling procedures presented in Chapter 4. Third, we obtain frames that list all elements in each of the sampled clusters. Finally, we select a simple random sample of elements from each of these frames.

9.3   Unbiased Estimation of a Population Mean and Total

As in previous chapters, we are interested in estimating a population mean, μ, or a population total, τ, and placing a bound on the error of estimation. The following notation is used:

N = the number of clusters in the population,

n = the number of clusters selected in a simple random sample,

M_i = the number of elements in cluster i,

m_i = the number of elements selected in a simple random sample from cluster i,

$M = \sum\limits_{i=1}^{N} M_i$ = the number of elements in the population,

$\overline{M} = \dfrac{M}{N}$ = the average cluster size for the population,

y_{ij} = the jth observation in the sample from the ith cluster,

and

$$\bar{y}_i = \frac{1}{m_i} \sum_{j=1}^{m_i} y_{ij} = \text{the sample mean for the } i\text{th cluster.}$$

Unbiased estimator of the population mean μ:

$$\hat{\mu} = \frac{N}{M} \frac{\sum_{i=1}^{n} M_i \bar{y}_i}{n}. \tag{9.1}$$

Estimated variance of $\hat{\mu}$:

$$\hat{V}(\hat{\mu}) = \left(\frac{N-n}{N}\right) \frac{1}{n\overline{M}^2} s_b^2 + \frac{1}{nN\overline{M}^2} \sum_{i=1}^{n} M_i^2 \left(\frac{M_i - m_i}{M_i}\right) \frac{s_i^2}{m_i}, \tag{9.2}$$

where

$$s_b^2 = \frac{\sum_{i=1}^{n} (M_i \bar{y}_i - \overline{M}\hat{\mu})^2}{n-1} \tag{9.3}$$

and

$$s_i^2 = \frac{\sum_{j=1}^{m_i} (y_{ij} - \bar{y}_i)^2}{m_i - 1}, \quad i = 1, \dots n. \tag{9.4}$$

Bound on the error of estimation:

$$2\sqrt{\hat{V}(\hat{\mu})}. \tag{9.5}$$

The estimator, $\hat{\mu}$, shown in equation (9.1), depends on M, the number of elements in the population. A method of estimating μ when M is unknown is given in the next section.

Note that s_i^2 is the sample variance for the sample selected from cluster i.

Example 9.1

A garment manufacturer has 90 plants located throughout the United States, and wants to estimate the average number of hours that his sewing machines were down for repairs in the past months. Because the plants are widely scattered, he decides to use cluster sampling, specifying each plant as a cluster of machines. Each plant contains many machines, and it would be time consuming to check the repair record for each machine. Therefore it seems appropriate to use two-stage sampling. Enough time and money is available to sample $n = 10$ plants and approximately 20% of the machines in each plant.

Using the data in Table 9.1, estimate the average downtime per machine and place a bound on the error of estimation. The manufacturer knows he has a combined total of 4500 machines in all plants.

Table 9.1 Downtime for sewing machines.

Plant	M_i	m_i	Downtime (in hours)	$\bar{y}_i$	s_i^2
1	50	10	5, 7, 9, 0, 11, 2, 8, 4, 3, 5	5.40	11.38
2	65	13	4, 3, 7, 2, 11, 0, 1, 9, 4, 3, 2, 1, 5	4.00	10.67
3	45	9	5, 6, 4, 11, 12, 0, 1, 8, 4	5.67	16.75
4	48	10	6, 4, 0, 1, 0, 9, 8, 4, 6, 10	4.80	13.29
5	52	10	11, 4, 3, 1, 0, 2, 8, 6, 5, 3	4.30	11.12
6	58	12	12, 11, 3, 4, 2, 0, 0, 1, 4, 3, 2, 4	3.83	14.88
7	42	8	3, 7, 6, 7, 8, 4, 3, 2	5.00	5.14
8	66	13	3, 6, 4, 3, 2, 2, 8, 4, 0, 4, 5, 6, 3	3.85	4.31
9	40	8	6, 4, 7, 3, 9, 1, 4, 5	4.88	6.13
10	56	11	6, 7, 5, 10, 11, 2, 1, 4, 0, 5, 4	5.00	11.80

Solution

The best estimate of μ is $\hat{\mu}$, shown in equation (9.1), which yields

$$\hat{\mu} = \frac{N}{Mn} \sum_{i=1}^{n} M_i \bar{y}_i$$

$$= \frac{90}{(4500)(10)} [(50)(5.40) + (65)(4.00) + \cdots + (56)(5.00)]$$

$$= \frac{90}{(4500)(10)} (2400.59) = 4.80.$$

In order to estimate the variance of $\hat{\mu}$, we must calculate

$$s_b^2 = \frac{1}{n-1} \sum_{i=1}^{n} (M_i \bar{y}_i - \bar{M}\hat{\mu})^2$$

$$= \frac{1}{n-1} \left[\sum_{i=1}^{n} (M_i \bar{y}_i)^2 - 2\bar{M}\hat{\mu} \sum_{i=1}^{n} M_i \bar{y}_i + n(\bar{M}\hat{\mu})^2 \right]$$

$$= \frac{1}{9} [583,198.6721 - 2(50)(4.80)(2400.59) + 10(240)^2]$$

$$= 768.38$$

and

$$\sum_{i=1}^{n} M_i^2 \left(\frac{M_i - m_i}{M_i} \right) \frac{s_i^2}{m_i}$$

$$= (50)^2 \left(\frac{50 - 10}{50} \right) \frac{11.38}{10} + \cdots + (56)^2 \left(\frac{56 - 11}{56} \right) \frac{11.80}{11}$$

$$= 21,990.96.$$

Then, from equation (9.2),

$$\hat{V}(\hat{\mu}) = \left(\frac{N-n}{N} \right) \frac{1}{n\bar{M}^2} s_b^2 + \frac{1}{nN\bar{M}^2} \sum_{i=1}^{n} M_i^2 \left(\frac{M_i - m_i}{M_i} \right) \frac{s_i^2}{m_i}$$

$$= \left(\frac{90 - 10}{90} \right) \frac{1}{(10)(50)^2} (768.38) + \frac{1}{(10)(90)(50)^2} (21,990.96)$$

$$= .037094.$$

The estimate of μ with a bound on the error of estimation is given by

$$\hat{\mu} \pm 2\sqrt{\hat{V}(\hat{\mu})},$$

$$4.80 \pm 2\sqrt{.037094},$$

or

$$4.80 \pm .38.$$

Thus, the average downtime is estimated to be 4.80 hours. The error of estimation should be less than .38 hours with a probability of approximately .95.

An unbiased estimator of a population total can be found by taking an unbiased estimator of the population mean and multiplying by the number of elements in the population in a manner similar to that used in simple random sampling. Thus, $M\hat{\mu}$ is an unbiased estimator of τ for two-stage cluster sampling.

Estimation of the population total τ:

$$\hat{\tau} = M\hat{\mu} = N \frac{\sum_{i=1}^{n} M_i \bar{y}_i}{n}. \tag{9.6}$$

Estimated variance of $\hat{\tau}$:

$$V(\hat{\tau}) = M^2 \hat{V}(\hat{\mu})$$

$$= \left(\frac{N-n}{N}\right) \frac{N^2}{n} s_b^2 + \frac{N}{n} \sum_{i=1}^{n} M_i^2 \left(\frac{M_i - m_i}{M_i}\right) \frac{s_i^2}{m_i}, \tag{9.7}$$

where s_b^2 is given by (9.3) and s_i^2 is given by (9.4).

Bound on the error of estimation:

$$2\sqrt{\hat{V}(\hat{\tau})} = 2\sqrt{M^2 \hat{V}(\hat{\mu})}. \tag{9.8}$$

Note that we do not need to know M in order to calculate $\hat{\tau}$ or the estimated variance of $\hat{\tau}$, since the M's cancel out in the formula for $\hat{\tau}$ and s_b^2 (see equations (9.6) and (9.7)).

Example 9.2

Estimate the total amount of downtime during the past month for all machines owned by the manufacturer in Example 9.1. Place a bound on the error of estimation.

Solution

The best estimate of τ is

$$\hat{\tau} = M\hat{\mu} = \frac{N}{n} \sum_{i=1}^{n} M_i \bar{y}_i$$

$$= \frac{90}{10} (2400.59) = 21{,}605.31.$$

The estimated variance of $\hat{\tau}$ is found using the value of $\hat{V}(\hat{\mu})$ calculated in Example 9.1 and substituting as follows:

$$\hat{V}(\hat{\tau}) = M^2 \hat{V}(\hat{\mu})$$

$$= (4500)^2(.037094).$$

The estimate of τ with a bound on the error of estimation is

$$\hat{\tau} \pm 2\sqrt{\hat{V}(\hat{\tau})},$$

$$21{,}605.31 \pm 2\sqrt{(4500)^2(.037094)},$$

or

$$21{,}605.31 \pm 1733.4.$$

Thus, the estimate of total downtime is 21,605.31 hours. We are fairly confident that the error of estimation is less than 1733.4 hours.

9.4   Ratio Estimation of a Population Mean

The estimator, $\hat{\mu}$, given by equation (9.1), depends upon the total number of elements in the population, M. When M is unknown, as is frequently the case, it must be estimated from the sample data. We obtain an estimator of M by multiplying the average cluster size, $\sum_{i=1}^{n} M_i/n$, by the number of clusters in the population, N. If we replace M by its estimator, we obtain a ratio estimator, denoted by $\hat{\mu}_r$, because the numerator and denominator are both random variables.

Ratio estimator of the population mean, μ:

$$\hat{\mu}_r = \frac{\sum\limits_{i=1}^{n} M_i \bar{y}_i}{\sum\limits_{i=1}^{n} M_i} \tag{9.9}$$

Estimated variance of $\hat{\mu}_r$:

$$\hat{V}(\hat{\mu}_r) = \left(\frac{N-n}{N}\right)\frac{1}{n\overline{M}^2}s_r^2 + \frac{1}{nN\overline{M}^2}\sum_{i=1}^{n}M_i^2\left(\frac{M_i - m_i}{M_i}\right)\frac{s_i^2}{m_i}, \tag{9.10}$$

where

$$s_r^2 = \frac{\sum\limits_{i=1}^{n} M_i^2(\bar{y}_i - \hat{\mu}_r)^2}{n-1} \tag{9.11}$$

and

$$s_i^2 = \frac{\sum\limits_{j=1}^{m_i}(y_{ij} - \bar{y}_i)^2}{m_i - 1}, \quad i = 1, \dots, n. \tag{9.12}$$

Bound on the error of estimation:

$$2\sqrt{\hat{V}(\hat{\mu}_r)}. \tag{9.13}$$

The estimator $\hat{\mu}_r$ is biased, but the bias is negligible when n is large.

Example 9.3

Using the data in Table 9.1, estimate the average downtime per machine and place a bound on the error of estimation. Assume the manufacturer does not know how many machines there are in all plants combined.

Solution

Because M is unknown, we must use $\hat{\mu}_r$, given by equation (9.9), to estimate μ. Our calculations yield

$$\hat{\mu}_r = \frac{\sum\limits_{i=1}^{n} M_i \bar{y}_i}{\sum\limits_{i=1}^{n} M_i}$$

$$= \frac{(50)(5.40) + (65)(4.00) + \cdots + (56)(5.00)}{50 + 65 + \cdots + 56}$$

$$= \frac{2400.59}{522} = 4.60.$$

To find the estimated variance of $\hat{\mu}_r$, we must calculate

$$s_r^2 = \frac{1}{n-1} \sum_{i=1}^{n} M_i^2 (\bar{y}_i - \hat{\mu}_r)^2$$

$$= \frac{1}{n-1} \left[\sum_{i=1}^{n} (M_i \bar{y}_i)^2 - 2\hat{\mu}_r \sum_{i=1}^{n} M_i^2 \bar{y}_i + (\hat{\mu}_r)^2 \sum_{i=1}^{n} M_i^2 \right]$$

$$= \frac{1}{9} [583,198.6721 - 2(4.60)(126,530.87)$$

$$\quad + (4.6)^2 (27,978)]$$

$$= 1236.57.$$

Note that, as in Example (9.1),

$$\sum_{i=1}^{n} M_i^2 \left(\frac{M_i - m_i}{M_i} \right) \frac{s_i^2}{m_i} = 21,990.96.$$

We can estimate $\bar{M}$ by using the average cluster size for the sample:

$$\frac{\sum_{i=1}^{n} M_i}{n} = \frac{522}{10} = 52.2.$$

Substituting into equation (9.10), the estimated variance of $\hat{\mu}_r$ is

$$\hat{V}(\hat{\mu}_r) = \left(\frac{N-n}{N} \right) \frac{1}{n\bar{M}^2} s_r^2 + \frac{1}{nN\bar{M}^2} \sum_{i=1}^{n} M_i^2 \left(\frac{M_i - m_i}{M_i} \right) \frac{s_i^2}{m_i}$$

$$= \left(\frac{90-10}{90} \right) \frac{1}{(10)(52.2)^2} (1236.57) + \frac{1}{10(90)(52.2)^2} (21,990.96)$$

$$= .049306.$$

The estimate of the average downtime with a bound on the error of estimation is

$$\hat{\mu}_r \pm 2 \sqrt{\hat{V}(\hat{\mu}_r)},$$

$$4.60 \pm 2 \sqrt{.049306},$$

or

$$4.60 \pm .44.$$

Thus, the estimated mean downtime per machine is 4.60 hours with a bound on the error of estimation of .44 hours.

9.5   Estimation of a Population Proportion

Consider the problem of estimating a population proportion, p, such as the proportion of university students in favor of a certain law or the proportion of machines which have had no downtime for the past month. An estimate of p can be obtained by using $\hat{\mu}$, given in equation (9.1), or $\hat{\mu}_r$, given in equation (9.9), and letting $y_{ij} = 1$ or 0 depending on whether or not the jth element in the ith cluster falls into the category of interest.

Because M is usually unknown, we present the formulas for estimating p with a ratio estimator analogous to $\hat{\mu}_r$, given in equation (9.9). Let $\hat{p}_i$ denote the proportion of sampled elements from cluster i which fall into the category of interest.

Estimator of a population proportion p:

$$\hat{p} = \frac{\sum\limits_{i=1}^{n} M_i \hat{p}_i}{\sum\limits_{i=1}^{n} M_i}. \tag{9.14}$$

Estimated variance of $\hat{p}$:

$$\hat{V}(\hat{p}) = \left(\frac{N-n}{N}\right) \frac{1}{n\overline{M}^2} s_r^2 + \frac{1}{nN\overline{M}^2} \sum_{i=1}^{n} M_i^2 \left(\frac{M_i - m_i}{M_i}\right) \frac{\hat{p}_i \hat{q}_i}{m_i - 1}, \tag{9.15}$$

where

$$s_r^2 = \frac{\sum\limits_{i=1}^{n} M_i^2 (\hat{p}_i - \hat{p})^2}{n-1} \tag{9.16}$$

and

$$\hat{q}_i = 1 - \hat{p}_i.$$

Bound on the error of estimation:

$$2\sqrt{\hat{V}(\hat{p})} \tag{9.17}$$

Example 9.4

The manufacturer in Example 9.1 wants to estimate the proportion of machines which have been shut down for major repairs (those requiring parts from stock outside the factory). The sample proportions of machines requiring major repairs are given in Table 9.2. The data are for the machines sampled in Exercise 9.1.

Estimate, p, the proportion of machines involved in major repairs for all plants combined, and place a bound on the error of estimation.

Table 9.2   Proportion of sewing machines requiring major repairs.

Plant	M_i	m_i	Proportion of machines requiring major repairs, $\hat{p}_i$
1	50	10	.40
2	65	13	.38
3	45	9	.22
4	48	10	.30
5	52	10	.50
6	58	12	.25
7	42	8	.38
8	66	13	.31
9	40	8	.25
10	56	11	.36

Solution

The best estimate of p is given by

$$\hat{p} = \frac{\sum\limits_{i=1}^{n} M_i \hat{p}_i}{\sum\limits_{i=1}^{n} M_i}$$

$$= \frac{50(.40) + 65(.38) + \cdots + 56(.36)}{50 + 65 + \cdots + 56}$$

$$= \frac{176.08}{522} = .34.$$

To estimate the variance of $\hat{p}$, we calculate

$$s_r^2 = \frac{1}{n-1} \sum\limits_{i=1}^{n} M_i^2 (\hat{p}_i - \hat{p})^2$$

$$= \frac{1}{n-1} \left[\sum\limits_{i=1}^{n} (M_i \hat{p}_i)^2 - 2\hat{p} \sum\limits_{i=1}^{n} M_i^2 \hat{p}_i + (\hat{p})^2 \sum\limits_{i=1}^{n} M_i^2 \right]$$

$$= \frac{1}{9} [3381.4688 - 2(.34)(9484.84) + (.34)^2(27,978)]$$

$$= 18.4482$$

and

$$\sum_{i=1}^{n} M_i^2 \left(\frac{M_i - m_i}{M_i} \right) \frac{\hat{p}_i \hat{q}_i}{m_i - 1}$$

$$= (50)^2 \left(\frac{50 - 10}{50} \right) \frac{(.4)(.6)}{9} + \cdots + (56)^2 \left(\frac{56 - 11}{56} \right) \frac{(.36)(.64)}{10}$$

$$= 509.4881.$$

Then the estimated variance of $\hat{p}$ when $\bar{M}$ is estimated by the sample average, 52.2, is

$$\hat{V}(\hat{p}) = \frac{N - n}{N} \frac{1}{n\bar{M}^2} s_r^2 + \frac{1}{nN\bar{M}^2} \sum_{i=1}^{n} M_i^2 \left(\frac{M_i - m_i}{M_i} \right) \frac{\hat{p}_i q_i}{m_i - 1}$$

$$= \left(\frac{90 - 10}{90} \right) \frac{1}{(10)(52.2)^2} (18.4482) + \frac{1}{(10)(90)(52.2)^2} (509.4881)$$

$$= .00081.$$

The best estimate of the proportion of machines which have undergone major repairs is

$$\hat{p} \pm 2\sqrt{\hat{V}(\hat{p})},$$

$$.34 \pm 2\sqrt{.00081},$$

or

$$.34 \pm .056.$$

We estimate the proportion of machines involved in major repairs to be .34, with a bound of .056 on the error of estimation.

9.6 Summary

The concept of cluster sampling can be extended to two-stage sampling by taking a simple random sample of elements from each sampled cluster. Two-stage cluster sampling is advantageous when a frame listing all elements in the population is not available or when it is desirable to have sample elements in geographic proximity because of travel costs.

Two-stage cluster sampling eliminates the need to sample all elements in each sampled cluster. Thus, the cost of sampling can often be reduced with little loss of information.

An unbiased estimator of μ is presented for the case when M, the total number of elements in the population, is known. When M is unknown, a ratio estimator is employed. Estimators are also given for a population total, τ, and for a population proportion, p.

References

Cochran, W. G., *Sampling Techniques*, 2d ed., New York: John Wiley and Sons, Inc., 1953.

Hansen, M. H., W. N. Hurwitz, and W. G. Madow, *Sampling Survey Methods and Theory*, Vol. 1, New York: John Wiley and Sons, Inc., 1953.

Kish, L., *Survey Sampling*, New York: John Wiley and Sons, Inc., 1965.

Exercises

9.1   A nurseryman wants to estimate the average height of seedlings in a large field that is divided into 50 plots that vary slightly in size. He believes the heights are fairly constant throughout each plot, but may vary considerably from plot to plot. Therefore, it is decided to sample 10% of the trees within each of 10 plots using a two-stage cluster sample. The data are as follows:

Plot	Number of seedlings	Number of seedlings sampled	Heights of seedlings (inches)
1	52	5	12, 11, 12, 10, 13
2	56	6	10, 9, 7, 9, 8, 10
3	60	6	6, 5, 7, 5, 6, 4
4	46	5	7, 8, 7, 7, 6
5	49	5	10, 11, 13, 12, 12
6	51	5	14, 15, 13, 12, 13
7	50	5	6, 7, 6, 8, 7
8	61	6	9, 10, 8, 9, 9, 10
9	60	6	7, 10, 8, 9, 9, 10
10	45	6	12, 11, 12, 13, 12, 12

Estimate the average height of seedlings in the field, and place a bound on the error of estimation.

9.2   In Exercise 9.1, assume that the nurseryman knows there are approximately 2600 seedlings in the field. Use this additional information to estimate the average height, and place a bound on the error of estimation.

9.3   A supermarket chain has stores in 32 cities. A company official wants to estimate the proportion of stores in the chain which do not meet a specified

cleanliness criterion. Stores within each city appear to possess similar characteristics; therefore it is decided to select a two-stage cluster sample containing
one-half of the stores within each of four cities. Cluster sampling is desirable
in this situation because of travel costs. The data collected are as follows:

City	Number of stores in city	Number of stores sampled	Number of stores not meeting criterion.
1	25	13	3
2	10	5	1
3	18	9	4
4	16	8	2

Estimate the proportion of stores not meeting the cleanliness criterion, and
place a bound on the error of estimation.

9.4   Repeat Exercise 9.3 given that the chain contains 450 stores.

9.5   To improve telephone service, an executive of a certain company wants to
estimate the total number of phone calls placed by secretaries in the company during one day. The company contains 12 departments, each making
approximately the same number of calls per day. Each department employs
approximately 20 secretaries, and the number of calls made varies considerably from secretary to secretary. It is decided to employ two-stage cluster
sampling using a small number of departments (clusters) and selecting a
fairly large number of secretaries (elements) from each. Ten secretaries are
sampled from each of four departments. The data are summarized in the
following table.

Department	Number of secretaries	Number of secretaries sampled	Mean $\bar{y}_i$	Variance s_i^2
1	21	10	15.5	2.8
2	23	10	15.8	3.1
3	20	10	17.0	3.5
4	20	10	14.9	3.4

Estimate the total number of calls placed by the secretaries in this company,
and place a bound on the error of estimation.

9.6   A city zoning commission wants to estimate the proportion of property
owners in a certain section of a city who favor a proposed zoning change.
The section is divided into 7 distinct residential areas, each containing
similar residents. Because the results must be obtained in a short period of
time, two-stage cluster sampling is used. Three of the 7 areas are selected at
random and 20% of the property owners in each area selected are sampled.
The figure of 20% seems reasonable because the people living within each
area seem to be in the same socioeconomic class and, hence, they tend to
hold similar opinions on the zoning question. The results are as follows:

Area	Number of property owners	Number of property owners sampled	Number in favor of zoning change
1	46	9	1
2	67	13	2
3	93	20	2

Estimate the proportion of property owners who favor the proposed zoning change, and place a bound on the error of estimation.

9.7   A forester wants to estimate the total number of trees in a certain county which are infected with a particular disease. There are ten well-defined forest areas in the county; these areas can be subdivided into plots of approximately the same size. Four crews are available to conduct the survey, which must be completed in one day. Hence, two-stage cluster sampling is used. Four areas (clusters) are chosen with 6 plots (elements) randomly selected from each. (Each crew can survey six plots in one day.) The data are as follows.

Area	Number of plots	Number of plots sampled	Number of infected trees per plot
1	12	6	15, 14, 21, 13, 9, 10
2	15	6	4, 6, 10, 9, 8, 5
3	14	6	10, 11, 14, 10, 9, 15
4	21	6	8, 3, 4, 1, 2, 5

Estimate the total number of infected trees in the county, and place a bound on the error of estimation.

9.8   A new bottling machine is being tested by a company. During a test run, the machine fills 24 cases, each containing a dozen bottles. It is desired to estimate the average number of ounces of fill per bottle. A two-stage cluster sample is employed using 6 cases (clusters) with 4 bottles (elements) randomly selected from each. The results are as follows:

Case	Average ounces of fill for sample ($\bar{y}_i$)	Sample variance (s_i^2)
1	7.9	.15
2	8.0	.12
3	7.8	.09
4	7.9	.11
5	8.1	.10
6	7.9	.12

Estimate the average number of ounces per bottle, and place a bound on the error of estimation.

10 Sampling from Wildlife Populations

10.1 Introduction

The estimation of population sizes is very important in the study of growth, evolution, and maintenance of many wildlife populations. Various techniques for sampling wildlife populations have been used for many years. We will discuss two procedures for obtaining an estimate of N, the total size of a wildlife population.

The first method is *direct sampling*. Basically, this procedure entails drawing a random sample from a wildlife population of interest, tagging each animal sampled, and returning the tagged animals to the population. At a later date another random sample (of a fixed size) is drawn from the same population, and the number of tagged animals is observed. If N represents the total population size, t represents the number of animals tagged in the initial sample, and p represents the proportion of tagged animals in the population, then

$$\frac{t}{N} = p.$$

Consequently, $N = t/p$. We can obtain an estimate of N because t is known and p can be estimated by $\hat{p}$, the proportion of tagged animals in the second sample.

Thus,

$$\hat{N} = \frac{\text{the number of animals tagged}}{\text{the proportion of tagged animals in the second sample}}$$

or, equivalently,

$$\hat{N} = \frac{t}{\hat{p}}.$$

The second technique is *inverse sampling*. It is similiar to direct sampling, but the second sample size is not fixed. That is, we sample until a fixed number of tagged animals is observed. Using this procedure, we can also obtain an estimate of N, the total population size, using

$$\hat{N} = \frac{t}{\hat{p}}.$$

10.2   Estimation of a Population Size Using Direct Sampling

Direct sampling can be used to estimate the size of a mobile population. First, a random sample of size t is drawn from the population of interest. At a later date a second sample of size n is drawn. For example, suppose a conservationist is concerned about the apparent decline in the number of seals in Alaska. Estimates of the population size are available from previous years. To determine whether or not there has been a decline, a random sample of $t = 200$ seals is caught, tagged, and then released. A month later a second sample of size $n = 100$ is obtained. Using these data (often called recapture data) we can estimate N, the population size.

Let s be the number of tagged individuals observed in the second sample. The proportion of tagged individuals in the sample is

$$\hat{p} = \frac{s}{n}.$$

An estimate of N is given by

$$\hat{N} = \frac{t}{\hat{p}} = \frac{nt}{s}.$$

Estimator of N:

$$\hat{N} = \frac{nt}{s}. \tag{10.1}$$

Estimated variance of N:

$$\hat{V}(\hat{N}) = \frac{t^2 n(n-s)}{s^3}. \tag{10.2}$$

Bound on the error of estimation:

$$2\sqrt{\hat{V}(\hat{N})} = 2\sqrt{\frac{t^2 n(n-s)}{s^3}}. \tag{10.3}$$

Note that s must be greater than 0 for equations (10.1), (10.2), and (10.3) to hold. We will assume that n is large enough to recapture at least one tagged animal, so that s is greater than 0.

You should also realize that $\hat{N}$, which is presented in equation (10.1), is not an unbiased estimator of N. For $s > 0$

$$E(\hat{N}) \approx N + \frac{N(N-t)}{nt}.$$

Hence, for fairly large sample sizes, i.e., t and n large, the term

$$\frac{N(N-t)}{nt}$$

is small and the bias of the estimator $\hat{N}$ approaches 0.

Example 10.1

Before posting a schedule for the upcoming hunting season, the game commission for a particular county wishes to estimate the size of the deer population. A random sample of 300 deer is captured ($t = 300$). The deer are tagged and released. A second sample of 200 is taken two weeks later ($n = 200$). If 62 tagged deer are recaptured in the second sample ($s = 62$), estimate N and place a bound on the error of estimation.

Solution

Using equation (10.1), we have

$$\hat{N} = \frac{nt}{s} = \frac{300(200)}{62} = 967.74,$$

or

$$\hat{N} = 968.$$

A bound on the error of estimation is given by

$$2\sqrt{\hat{V}(\hat{N})} = 2\sqrt{\frac{t^2 n(n-s)}{s^3}}$$

$$= 2\sqrt{\frac{(300)^2(200)(138)}{(62)^3}}$$

$$= 148.67.$$

Thus, the game commission estimates the total number of deer is 968 with a bound on the error of estimation of approximately 149 deer.

You may be concerned about the magnitude of the bound on the error of estimation in this example. As might be expected, we can obtain a more accurate estimator of N by increasing the two sample sizes (n and t). Further information on the choice of t and n is given in Section 10.4.

10.3   Estimation of a Population Size Using Inverse Sampling

Inverse sampling is the second method for estimating N, the total size of a population. We again assume that an initial sample of t individuals is drawn, tagged, and released. Later, random sampling is conducted until exactly s tagged animals are recaptured. If the sample contains n individuals, the proportion of tagged individuals in the sample is given by $\hat{p} = s/n$. We use this sample proportion to estimate the proportion of tagged individuals in the population.

Again, the estimator of N is given by

$$\hat{N} = \frac{t}{\hat{p}} = \frac{nt}{s}.$$

Estimator of N:

$$\hat{N} = \frac{nt}{s}. \tag{10.4}$$

Estimated variance of $\hat{N}$:

$$\hat{V}(\hat{N}) = \frac{t^2 n(n - s)}{s^2(s + 1)}. \tag{10.5}$$

Bound on the error of estimation:

$$2\sqrt{\hat{V}(\hat{N})} = 2\sqrt{\frac{t^2 n(n - s)}{s^2(s + 1)}}. \tag{10.6}$$

Note that equations (10.4), (10.5), and (10.6) hold only for $s > 0$. This restriction offers no difficulty: we simply specify that s must be greater than 0, and we sample until s tagged individuals are recaptured. The estimator $\hat{N} = t/s$ obtained using inverse sampling provides an unbiased estimator of N.

Example 10.2

Authorities of a large wildlife preserve are interested in the total number of birds of a particular species that inhabits the preserve. A random sample of $t = 150$ birds is trapped, tagged, and then released. In the same month a second sample is drawn until 35 tagged birds are recaptured ($s = 35$). In total, 100 birds are recaptured in order to find 35 tagged ones ($n = 100$). Estimate N and place a bound on the error of estimation.

Solution

Using equation (10.4), we estimate N by

$$\hat{N} = \frac{nt}{s} = \frac{100(150)}{35} = 428.57.$$

A bound on the error of estimation is found by using equation (10.6) as follows:

$$2\sqrt{\hat{V}(\hat{N})} = 2\sqrt{\frac{t^2 n(n-s)}{s^2(s+1)}}$$

$$= 2\sqrt{\frac{(150)^2(100)(65)}{(35)^2(36)}}$$

$$= 115.173.$$

Hence, we estimate that 429 birds of the particular species inhabit the preserve. We are quite confident that our estimate is within approximately 116 birds of the true population size.

10.4   Choosing Sample Sizes for Direct and Inverse Sampling

We have been discussing direct sampling and inverse sampling techniques. You probably wonder which is the better procedure to use. Either method can be used. Inverse sampling yields more precise information than does direct sampling, provided the second sample size, n, required to recapture s tagged individuals is small relative to the population size, N. However, if nothing is known about the size of N, a poor choice of t could make n quite large when inverse sampling is used. For example, if $N = 10,000$ and a first sample of $t = 50$ individuals is drawn, it would take a large second sample to obtain exactly $s = 10$ tagged animals.

Table 10.1 is useful in determining the sample sizes (t and n) required to estimate $\hat{N}$ with a fixed bound on the error of estimation. However, to use these data requires some prior knowledge concerning the magnitude of N. Entries in Tables 10.1 are $V(\hat{N})/N$ for direct sampling. If you know the approximate size of N, you can determine the variance of the estimator for fixed values of the sample sizes t and n. In Table 10.1, these sample sizes are expressed as fractions of N. These fractions, given by

$$p_1 = \frac{t}{N} \quad \text{and} \quad p_2 = \frac{n}{N},$$

are called sampling fractions.

Table 10.1 Values of $\dfrac{V(\hat{N})}{N}$ for Direct Sampling.

$p_2 = \dfrac{n}{N}$	$p_1 = \dfrac{t}{N}$ .001	.01	.1	.25	.50	1.0
.001	999000	99000	9000	3000	1000	0
.01	99900	9900	900	300	100	0
.1	9990	990	90	30	10	0
.25	3996	396	36	12	4	0
.50	1998	198	18	6	2	0
1.0	999	99	9	3	1	0

It would be convenient to have a graph of the entries in this table. However, the numbers are so large that we can only display a portion of Table 10.1.

In Figure 10.1 we display the values of $V(\hat{N})/N$ for various values of the

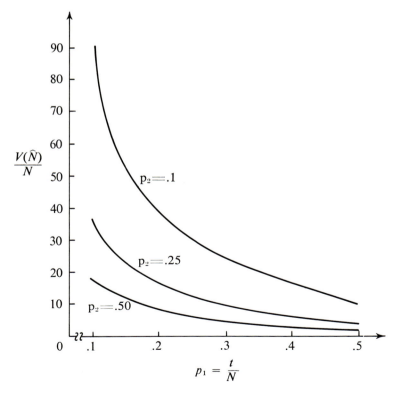

Figure 10.1

sampling fractions $p_1 = t/N$ and $p_2 = n/N$. Note that as either p_1 or p_2 increases, the variance of $\hat{N}$ divided by N decreases; consequently $V(\hat{N})$ decreases for a fixed value of N. Intuitively this makes sense since we should obtain a more accurate estimate of N by taking large sample sizes.

Example 10.3

The game commission in Example 10.1 believes that the size of the deer population is approximately the same as in the preceding year when there were between 800 and 1000 deer. Determine the bound on the error of estimation associated with the sampling fractions of $p_1 = .25$ and $p_2 = .25$.

Solution

We take the larger of the two figures (N approximately 1000) to obtain a conservative estimate of $V(\hat{N})$ (one that is larger than would be expected). We see from Figure 10.1 (or Table 10.1) that the sampling fractions of $p_1 = t/N = .25$ and $p_2 = s/N = .25$ yield

$$\frac{V(\hat{N})}{N} = 12.$$

Taking $N = 1000$, we have

$$V(\hat{N}) = 1000(12) = 12000$$

and

$$\sqrt{V(\hat{N})} = \sqrt{12000} = 109.541.$$

The corresponding bound on the error of estimation is

$$2\sqrt{V(\hat{N})} = 2(109.541) = 219.082.$$

An investigator could use this information to plan his survey. If this bound on the error of estimation is acceptable, he could run a survey using $p_1 = .25$ and $p_2 = .25$; that is, he could draw an initial sample of

$$t = p_1 N = (.25)(1000) = 250$$

and a second sample of

$$n = p_2 N = (.25)(1000) = 250.$$

He could then estimate N using the data from the survey. The bound on the error of estimation should be approximately equal to 220, provided the original range for N is accurate.

If the bound on the error for $\hat{N}$ is not acceptable using the sampling fractions of $p_1 = p_2 = .25$, the investigator can work with Table 10.1 (or Figure 10.1) to determine the sampling fractions required to achieve an acceptable bound on the error of estimation.

Table 10.2   Values of $\dfrac{V(\hat{N})}{N}$ for Inverse Sampling

$p_2 = \dfrac{s}{N}$ \\ $p_1 = \dfrac{t}{N}$	.001	.01	.1	.25	.50	1.0
.001	999	990	900	750	500	0
.01	99.9	99.0	90.0	75.0	50.0	0
.1	9.99	9.90	9.00	7.50	5.00	0
.25	3.996	3.96	3.60	3.00	2.00	0
.50	1.998	1.98	1.80	1.50	1.00	0
1.0	0.999	0.99	0.90	0.75	0.50	0

We can examine $V(\hat{N})$ for inverse sampling in the same manner as for direct sampling. Entries in Table 10.2 are the values of $V(\hat{N})/N$ for various sampling fractions $p_1 = t/N$ and $p_2 = s/N$ when inverse sampling is used. You recall that in inverse sampling we fix s rather than n; hence the second sampling fraction is in terms of s. A graphical representation of these data would be helpful, but again the numbers are too large to plot conveniently. A portion of Table 10.2 is presented in Figure 10.2.

Note that $V(\hat{N})/N$ (or, equivalently, $V(\hat{N})$ for a given value of N) decreases as p_1 and p_2 increase. If the experimenter has an approximate range for N, he could use either Figure 10.2 or Table 10.2 to determine the sampling fractions $(p_1 = t/N, \ p_2 = s/N)$ necessary to achieve a reasonable bound. Then he could conduct a survey with an initial sample of

$$t = p_1 N.$$

The experimenter would begin taking a second sample at a future time and continue until

$$s = p_2 N$$

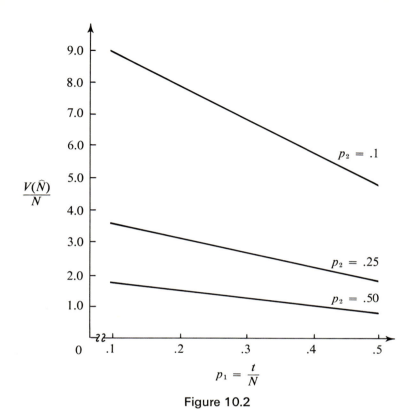

$$\frac{V(\widehat{N})}{N}$$

$$p_2 = .1$$

$$p_2 = .25$$

$$p_2 = .50$$

$$p_1 = \frac{t}{N}$$

Figure 10.2

tagged animals are recaptured. The corresponding bound on the error of estimation for N would be acceptable provided the original estimate for N was reasonable. Additional discussion of these and related topics can be found by consulting the references at the end of this chapter.

10.5   Summary

Estimation of the size of a population is often very important when studying mobile animal populations. Chapter 10 presents two procedures for estimating the total population size, N.

The first technique is direct sampling. A random sample of t individuals is drawn from a population and tagged. At a later date a fixed random sample of size n is drawn and the number of tagged individuals is observed. Using these data, one can estimate N and place a bound on the error of estimation.

The second technique, inverse sampling, is similar to direct sampling with the exception that we continue sampling until a fixed number, s, of tagged individuals is recaptured in the second sample. The sample data are then used to estimate N and to place a bound on the error of estimation.

When a choice is available between inverse and direct sampling procedures, inverse procedure appears to provide more accurate results. However, in some instances, particularly when little or nothing is known concerning the relative size of N, the direct sampling procedure is the better choice.

References

Bailey, Norman T. J., "On Estimating the Size of Mobile Populations from Recapture Data," *Biometrika* **38** (1951), 292–306.

Chapman, Douglas G., "Inverse, Multiple and Sequential Sample Censuses," *Biometrics* **8** (1952), 286–306.

Lovelace, Charles M., "The Mobility and Composition of Bobwhite Quail Populations in South Florida," Florida Game and Fresh Water Fish Commission Technical Report No. 4, (1958).

Exercises

10.1   Discuss the differences between direct and inverse sampling.

10.2   Name the restriction implicit in the use of (a) direct sampling, or (b) inverse sampling. How can this restriction be satisfied in each case?

10.3   Assuming the cost of sampling is not significant, how can one improve the bound on the error of estimation using either direct or inverse sampling?

10.4   A particular sportsmen's club is concerned about the number of brook trout in a certain stream. During a period of several days, $t = 100$ trout are caught, tagged, and then returned to the stream. Note that the sample represents 100 different fish; hence any fish caught during these dates which had already been tagged was immediately released. Several weeks later a second sample of $n = 120$ trout is caught and observed. If 27 in the second sample were tagged ($s = 27$), estimate N, the total size of the population, and place a bound on the error of estimation.

10.5   Wildlife biologists wish to estimate the total size of the bobwhite quail population in a section of southern Florida. A series of 50 traps is used.

In the first sample $t = 320$ quail are caught. After being captured each bird is removed from the trap and tagged with a metal band on its left leg. All birds are then released.

   Several months later a second sample of $n = 515$ quail is obtained. If $s = 91$ of these birds have tags, estimate N and place a bound on the error of estimation.

10.6   A game commission is interested in estimating the number of large-mouth bass in a reservoir. A random sample of $t = 2876$ bass is caught. Each bass is marked and released. One month later a second sample of $n = 2562$ is caught. If $s = 678$ have tags in the second sample, estimate the total population size. Place a bound on the error of estimation.

10.7   A team of conservationists is interested in estimating the size of the pheasant population in a particular area prior to the hunting season. The team believes that the true population size is between 2000 and 3000. Assuming $N \approx 3000$, the sampling fractions of p_1 and p_2 equal to .25 should give a bound on the error of estimation approximately equal to $2(189.74) = 379.48$ (Figure 10.1). The conservationists feel that this bound on the error is reasonable and so decide to choose $t = 750$ and $n = 750$. By using traps, they catch 750 pheasants for the first sample. Each of these pheasants is tagged and released. Several weeks later the second sample of $n = 750$ is obtained. If 168 of these pheasants have tags ($s = 168$), estimate the population size and place a bound on the error of estimation.

10.8   City officials are concerned about the nuisance caused by pigeons around city hall. To emphasize the problem, they hire a team of investigators to estimate the number of pigeons occupying the building. Using several different traps, a sample of $t = 60$ pigeons is captured, tagged, and re-leased. One month later the process is repeated using $n = 60$. If $s = 18$ tagged pigeons are observed in the second sample, estimate N and place a bound on the error of estimation.

10.9   Animal resource experts on a particular game preserve are concerned about an apparent decline in the rabbit population. In a study conducted two years ago, the population size was estimated to be $N = 2500$. Assume the population size is still of this magnitude and use Figure 10.1 to deter-mine the approximate sample sizes (t and n) required to estimate N with a bound equal to 356.

10.10 A zoologist wishes to estimate the size of the turtle population in a given geographical area. He believes that the turtle population size is between 500 and 1000; hence, an initial sample of 100 (10%) appears to be sufficient. The $t = 100$ turtles are caught, tagged, and released. A second sampling is begun one month later and it is decided to continue sampling until $s = 15$ tagged turtles are recaptured. If it takes 160 turtles to obtain 15 tagged turtles ($n = 160$, $s = 15$), estimate N and place a bound on the error of estimation.

10.11 Due to a particularly harsh winter, state park officials are concerned about the number of squirrels inhabiting their parks. An initial sample of $t = 100$ squirrels is trapped, tagged, and released. As soon as the first sample is completed, the officials begin working on a second sample of $n = 75$. They trap 10 squirrels that were tagged previously. Estimate N and place a bound on the error of estimation.

10.12 Assume the costs of taking an observation in the first sample and in the second sample are the same. Determine which is the most desirable: to have $t > n$, $t = n$, or $t < n$ for a fixed cost of conducting the two samples. (*Hint:* Consult Figures 10.1 and 10.2.)

10.13 A team of wildlife ecologists is interested in the effectiveness of an antifertility drug in controlling the growth of pigeon populations. To measure effectiveness, they will estimate the size of the population this year and compare it to the estimated size for a previous year. A large trap was constructed for the experiment. The trap was then baited with a corn feed containing a fixed amount of the drug. An initial sample of $t = 120$ pigeons is trapped and allowed to eat the medicated feed. Each bird is then tagged on its leg and released. At a later date, a second sample of $n = 100$ pigeons is trapped. If 48 of these birds have tags ($s = 48$), estimate the size of the pigeon population and place a bound on the error of estimation.

11 Supplemental Topics

11.1 Introduction

Four sample survey designs, simple and stratified random sampling, cluster sampling, and systematic sampling, have been discussed in preceding chapters. For each design it was assumed that the data were correctly recorded and provided an accurate representation of the n elements sampled from the population of interest. Under these assumptions, we were able to estimate certain population parameters and place a bound on the error of estimation.

There are many situations in which the assumptions underlying these designs are not fulfilled. First, the recorded measurements are not always accurate representations of the desired data, because of biases of the interviewers or measuring equipment. Second, the frame is not always adequate and, hence, the sample might not have been selected from the complete population of interest. Third, accurate sample data might be impossible to obtain because of the sensitive nature of the questions.

In this chapter, we give some methods for analyzing data when measurement errors are present or an inadequate frame is used.

11.2   Interpenetrating Subsamples

An experimenter is interested in obtaining information from a simple random sample of n persons selected from a population of size N. He has k interviewers available to do the field work, but the interviewers differ in their manner of interviewing and, hence, they obtain slightly different responses from identical subjects. For example, suppose the interviewer is to rate the health of a respondent on a scale from 0 to 5, with 0 denoting poor health. Obtaining this type of data requires skill in interviewing and a subjective judgment by the interviewer. One interviewer might not obtain enough information and might tend to rate the health of an individual too high, while another might obtain detailed information and tend to rate the health too low.

A good estimate of the population mean can be obtained by using the following technique. Randomly divide the n sampled elements into k subsamples of m elements each, and assign one interviewer to each of the k subsamples. Note that $m = n/k$ and n can always be chosen so that m is an integer. We consider the first subsample to be a simple random sample of size m selected from the n elements in the total sample. The second subsample is then a simple random sample of size m selected from the $n - m$ remaining elements. This process is continued until the n elements have been randomly divided into k subsamples. The k subsamples are sometimes called *interpenetrating subsamples*.

We expect some interviewers to give measurements which are too small and some too large, but the average of all sample measurements should be close to the population mean. That is, we expect the biases of the investigators to possess an average that is very near zero. Thus, the sample mean, $\bar{y}$, is the best estimator of the population mean, μ, even though the measurements are biased.

We use the following notation. Let y_{ij} denote the jth observation in the ith subsample, $j = 1, \ldots, m$, $i = 1, \ldots, k$. Then $\bar{y}_i$, given by

$$\bar{y}_i = \frac{1}{m} \sum_{j=1}^{m} y_{ij}, \tag{11.1}$$

is the average of all observations in the ith subsample. The sample mean, $\bar{y}$, is the average of the k subsample means.

Estimator of the population mean μ:

$$\bar{y} = \frac{1}{k} \sum_{i=1}^{k} \bar{y}_i. \tag{11.2}$$

Estimated variance of $\bar{y}$:

$$\hat{V}(\bar{y}) = \left(\frac{N-n}{N}\right) \frac{\sum\limits_{i=1}^{k}(\bar{y}_i - \bar{y})^2}{k(k-1)}. \tag{11.3}$$

Bound on the error of estimation:

$$2\sqrt{\hat{V}(\bar{y})} = 2\sqrt{\left(\frac{N-n}{n}\right) \frac{\sum\limits_{i=1}^{k}(\bar{y}_i - \bar{y})^2}{k(k-1)}}. \tag{11.4}$$

The technique of interpenetrating subsamples gives an estimate of the variance of $\bar{y}$, given in equation (11.3), which accounts for interviewer biases. That is, the estimated variance given in equation (11.3) is usually larger than the standard estimate of the variance of a sample mean obtained in simple random sampling because of the biases present in the measurements.

Example 11.1

A sociologist wants to estimate the average height of adult males in a community containing 800 men. He has 10 assistants, each with his own equipment, to acquire the measurements. Since the experimenter believes the assistants will produce slightly biased measurements, he decides to take a simple random sample of $n = 80$ males from the population and randomly divide the sample into 10 subsamples of 8 persons each. Each assistant is then assigned to one subsample. The measurements produce the following subsample means (measurements in feet):

$$\begin{array}{ll}
\bar{y}_1 = 5.9 & \bar{y}_6 = 5.7 \\
\bar{y}_2 = 5.8 & \bar{y}_7 = 5.8 \\
\bar{y}_3 = 6.1 & \bar{y}_8 = 5.6 \\
\bar{y}_4 = 6.0 & \bar{y}_9 = 5.9 \\
\bar{y}_5 = 6.1 & \bar{y}_{10} = 6.0
\end{array}$$

Estimate the mean height of adult males in the community, and place a bound on the error of estimation.

Solution

The best estimate of the population mean is the sample mean, $\bar{y}$. Thus, from equation (11.2),

$$\bar{y} = \frac{1}{k}\sum_{i=1}^{k}\bar{y}_i = \frac{1}{10}(5.9 + 5.8 + \cdots + 6.0)$$

$$= 5.89.$$

We must now estimate the variance of $\bar{y}$ using equation (11.3). The following identity is easily established:

$$\sum_{i=1}^{k} (\bar{y}_i - \bar{y})^2 = \sum_{i=1}^{k} \bar{y}_i^2 - \frac{\left(\sum_{i=1}^{k} \bar{y}_i\right)^2}{k}.$$

Substituting, we obtain

$$\sum_{i=1}^{k} (\bar{y}_i - \bar{y})^2 = 347.17 - \frac{(58.9)^2}{10} = .25.$$

Then,

$$\hat{V}(\bar{y}) = \left(\frac{N-n}{N}\right) \frac{\sum_{i=1}^{k} (\bar{y}_i - \bar{y})^2}{k(k-1)}$$

$$= \left(\frac{800-80}{800}\right)\left(\frac{.25}{10(9)}\right)$$

$$= .0025.$$

The estimate of the mean height of adult males with a bound on the error of estimation is given by

$$\bar{y} \pm 2\sqrt{\hat{V}(\bar{y})},$$

$$5.89 \pm 2\sqrt{.0025},$$

or

$$5.89 \pm .10.$$

To summarize, the best estimate of the mean height is 5.89 feet and we are reasonably confident that our error of estimation is less than .10 feet.

11.3   Estimation of Means and Totals over Subpopulations

It is often impossible to obtain a frame that lists only those elements in the population of interest. For example, we may wish to sample households containing children, but the best frame available may be a list of all households in a city. We may be interested in a firm's overdue accounts, but the only frame available may list all of the firm's accounts receivable. In situations of this type, we wish to estimate parameters of a subpopulation of the population represented in the frame. Sampling is complicated because we do not know whether an element belongs to the subpopulation until after it has been sampled.

The problem of estimating a subpopulation mean is solved essentially in the same manner as in Chapter 4. Let N denote the number of elements in the population and N_1 the number of elements in the subpopulation of interest. A simple random sample of n elements is selected from the population of N elements. Let n_1 denote the number of sampled elements which are from the subpopulation of interest. Let y_{1j} denote the jth sampled observation that falls in the sub-population. Then, the sample mean for elements from the subpopulation, denoted by $\bar{y}_1$, is given by

$$\bar{y}_1 = \frac{1}{n_1} \sum_{j=1}^{n_1} y_{1j}.$$

The sample mean, $\bar{y}_1$, is an unbiased estimate of the subpopulation mean, μ_1.

Estimator of the subpopulation mean μ_1:

$$\bar{y}_1 = \frac{1}{n_1} \sum_{j=1}^{n_1} y_{1j}. \tag{11.5}$$

Estimated variance of $\bar{y}_1$:

$$\hat{V}(\bar{y}_1) = \left(\frac{N_1 - n_1}{N_1}\right) \frac{\sum_{j=1}^{n_1} (y_{1j} - \bar{y}_1)^2}{n_1(n_1 - 1)}. \tag{11.6}$$

Bound on the error of estimation:

$$2\sqrt{\hat{V}(\bar{y}_1)} = 2\sqrt{\left(\frac{N_1 - n_1}{N_1}\right) \frac{\sum_{j=1}^{n_1} (y_{1j} - \bar{y}_1)^2}{n_1(n_1 - 1)}}. \tag{11.7}$$

The quantity $\dfrac{N_1 - n_1}{N_1}$ can be estimated by $\dfrac{N - n}{N}$ if N_1 is unknown.

Example 11.2

An economist wants to estimate the average weekly amount spent on food by families with children in a certain county known to be a poverty area. A complete list of all of the 250 families in the county is available, but it is impossible to identify those families with children. The economist selects a simple random sample of $n = 50$ families and finds that $n_1 = 42$ families have at least one child. The 42 families with children are interviewed and give the following information:

$$\sum_{j=1}^{42} y_{1j} = \$1,720, \qquad \sum_{j=1}^{42} y_{1j}^2 = 72,200.$$

Estimate the average weekly amount spent on food by all families with children, and place a bound on the error of estimation.

Solution

The estimator of the population mean is $\bar{y}_1$, given by equation (11.5). Calculations yield

$$\bar{y}_1 = \frac{1}{n_1} \sum_{j=1}^{n_1} y_{1j} = \frac{1}{42}(1720) = 40.95.$$

We have the equality

$$\sum_{j=1}^{n_1}(y_{1j} - \bar{y}_1)^2 = \sum_{j=1}^{n_1} y_{1j}^2 - \frac{1}{n_1}\left(\sum_{j=1}^{n_1} y_{1j}\right)^2,$$

and substituting,

$$\sum_{j=1}^{n_1}(y_{1j} - \bar{y}_1)^2 = 72,200 - \frac{1}{42}(1720)^2$$

$$= 1762.$$

The quantity $(N_1 - n_1)/N_1$ must be estimated by $(N - n)/N$, since N_1 is unknown. The estimated variance of $\bar{y}_1$, given in equation (11.6), then becomes

$$\hat{V}(\bar{y}_1) = \left(\frac{N-n}{N}\right)\frac{\sum_{j=1}^{n_1}(y_{1j} - \bar{y}_1)^2}{n_1(n_1 - 1)}$$

$$= \left(\frac{250 - 50}{250}\right)\frac{1762}{42(41)}$$

$$= .819.$$

Thus, the estimate of the population average with a bound in the error of estimation is given by

$$\bar{y}_1 \pm 2\sqrt{\hat{V}(\bar{y}_1)},$$

$$40.95 \pm 2\sqrt{.819},$$

or

$$40.95 \pm 1.81.$$

Our best estimate of the average weekly amount spent on food by families with children is \$40.95. The error of estimation should be less than \$1.81 with probability approximately .95.

If the number of elements in the subpopulation, N_1, is known, the subpopulation total, τ_1, can be estimated by $N_1 \bar{y}_1$.

Estimator of the subpopulation total τ_1:

$$N_1 \bar{y}_1 = \frac{N_1}{n_1} \sum_{j=1}^{n_1} y_{1j}. \qquad (11.8)$$

Estimated variance of $N_1 \bar{y}_1$:

$$\hat{V}(N_1 \bar{y}_1) = N_1^2 \hat{V}(\bar{y}_1) = N_1^2 \left(\frac{N_1 - n_1}{N_1} \right) \frac{\sum_{j=1}^{n_1} (y_{1j} - \bar{y}_1)^2}{n_1(n_1 - 1)}. \qquad (11.9)$$

Bound on the error of estimation:

$$2\sqrt{\hat{V}(N_1 \bar{y}_1)} = 2\sqrt{ N_1^2 \left(\frac{N_1 - n_1}{N_1} \right) \frac{\sum_{j=1}^{n_1} (y_{1j} - \bar{y}_1)^2}{n_1(n_1 - 1)} }. \qquad (11.10)$$

Example 11.3

A recent preliminary study of the county in Example 11.2 reveals $N_1 = 205$ families with children. Using this information and the data given in

Example 11.2, estimate the total weekly amount spent on food by families with children. (Note: N_1 will vary over time. We assume that the value of N_1 used in this analysis is correct.)

Solution

The best estimator of the total is $N_1 \bar{y}_1$, given in equation (11.8), which yields an estimate of

$$N_1 \bar{y}_1 = 205(40.95) = 8,394.75.$$

The quantity $\sum_{j=1}^{n_1} (y_{1j} - \bar{y}_1)^2$ is calculated in Example 11.2 to be 1762. The estimated variance of $N_1 \bar{y}_1$ is then (from equation (11.9))

$$\hat{V}(N_1 \bar{y}_1) = N_1^2 \left(\frac{N_1 - n_1}{N_1} \right) \frac{\sum_{j=1}^{n_1} (y_{1j} - \bar{y}_1)^2}{n_1(n_1 - 1)}$$

$$= (205)^2 \left(\frac{205 - 42}{205} \right) \frac{1762}{42(41)}$$

$$= 34,191.19.$$

The estimate of the total weekly amount that families with children spend on food, given with a bound on the error of estimation, is

$$N_1 \bar{y}_1 \pm 2\sqrt{\hat{V}(N_1 \bar{y}_1)},$$

$$8,394.75 \pm 2\sqrt{34,191.19}$$

or

$$8,394.75 \pm 369.82.$$

Frequently the number of elements in the subpopulation, N_1, is unknown. For example, it would be difficult to determine the exact number of households containing children in a city, whereas the total number of households could perhaps be obtained from a city directory. An unbiased estimate of τ can still be obtained even though N_1 is unknown.

Estimator of the subpopulation total, τ_1, when N_1 is unknown:

$$\hat{\tau}_1 = \frac{N}{n} \sum_{j=1}^{n_1} y_{1j}. \tag{11.11}$$

Estimated variance of $\hat{\tau}_1$:

$$\hat{V}(\hat{\tau}_1) = N^2 \left(\frac{N-n}{N}\right) \frac{\displaystyle\sum_{j=1}^{n_1} y_{1j}^2 - \frac{\left(\displaystyle\sum_{j=1}^{n_1} y_{1j}\right)^2}{n}}{n(n-1)}. \tag{11.12}$$

Bound on the error of estimation:

$$2\sqrt{\hat{V}(\hat{\tau}_1)} = 2\sqrt{ N^2 \left(\frac{N-n}{N}\right) \frac{\displaystyle\sum_{j=1}^{n_1} y_{1j}^2 - \frac{\left(\displaystyle\sum_{j=1}^{n_1} y_{1j}\right)^2}{n}}{n(n-1)} } \tag{11.13}$$

Example 11.4

Suppose that the experimenter in Example 11.3 doubts the accuracy of the preliminary value of N_1. Use the data of Example 11.3 to estimate the total weekly amount spent on food by families with children without using the value given for N_1.

Solution

The estimator of the total which does not depend on N_1 is $\hat{\tau}_1$, given by equation (11.11). Thus,

$$\hat{\tau}_1 = \frac{N}{n} \sum_{j=1}^{n_1} y_{1j} = \frac{250}{50} (1720) = 8600$$

Substituting into equation (11.12), the estimated variance of $\hat{\tau}_1$ is

$$\hat{V}(\hat{\tau}_1) = N^2 \left(\frac{N-n}{N}\right) \frac{\displaystyle\sum_{j=1}^{n_1} y_{1j}^2 - \frac{1}{n}\left(\displaystyle\sum_{j=1}^{n_1} y_{1j}\right)^2}{n(n-1)}$$

$$= (250)^2 \left(\frac{250-50}{250}\right) \left(\frac{72,200 - \frac{1}{50}(1720)^2}{50(49)}\right)$$

$$= 265,960.$$

Thus, the estimate of the total weekly amount spent on food with a bound on the error of estimation is

$$\hat{\tau}_1 \pm 2\sqrt{\hat{V}(\hat{\tau}_1)},$$

$$8600 \pm 2\sqrt{265{,}960},$$

or

$$8600 \pm 1031.44$$

This is a large bound on the error of estimation and should be reduced by increasing the sample size, n.

Note that the variance of $\hat{\tau}_1$, calculated in Example 11.4, is much larger than the variance of $N_1 \bar{y}_1$, calculated in Example 11.3. This is because the information provided by N_1 is used in $N_1 \bar{y}_1$ but not in $\hat{\tau}_1$. Thus, if N_1 is known, or if it can be found with little additional cost, the estimator $N_1 \bar{y}_1$ should be used.

11.4   Random Response Model

A person being interviewed often refuses to answer or give correct answers to sensitive questions which may embarrass him or be harmful to him in some way. For example, some persons may not respond truthfully to political questions such as, "Are you a Communist?" In this section, we present a method of estimating the proportion of people who have some characteristic of interest without obtaining direct answers from the people interviewed. The method is due to S. L. Warner (see the reference at the end of the chapter).

Designate the people in the population who have or do not have the characteristic of interest as Groups A and B, respectively. Thus, each person in the population is in either Group A or Group B. Let p be the proportion of people in Group A. The objective is to estimate p without asking each person directly whether or not he belongs to Group A. We can estimate p by using a device called a *random response model*. We start with a stack of cards which are identical except that a fraction, θ, are marked with A and the remaining fraction $(1 - \theta)$ are marked with B. A simple random sample of n people is selected from the population. Each person in the sample is asked to randomly draw a card from the deck and to state "yes" if the letter on the card agrees with the group to which he belongs, or "no" if the letter on the card is different from the group to which he belongs. The card is replaced before the next person draws. The interviewer does not see the card and simply records whether the response is "yes" or "no." Let n_1 be the number of people in the sample who respond with "yes." An unbiased estimator, $\hat{p}$, of the population proportion, p, is given in equation (11.14).

Estimator of a population proportion p:

$$\hat{p} = \frac{\theta - 1}{2\theta - 1} + \frac{n_1}{(2\theta - 1)n}. \tag{11.14}$$

Estimated variance of $\hat{p}$:

$$\hat{V}(\hat{p}) = \frac{1}{n}\left[\frac{1}{16\left(\theta - \frac{1}{2}\right)^2} - \left(\hat{p} - \frac{1}{2}\right)^2 \right]. \tag{11.15}$$

Bound on the error of estimation:

$$2\sqrt{\hat{V}(\hat{p})} = 2\sqrt{\frac{1}{n}\left[\frac{1}{16\left(\theta - \frac{1}{2}\right)^2} - \left(\hat{p} - \frac{1}{2}\right)^2 \right]}. \tag{11.16}$$

Equations (11.14), (11.15), and (11.16) are based on the assumption that the population size is large relative to n, so that the finite population correction can be ignored. The fraction, θ, of cards marked A may be arbitrarily chosen by the experimenter but must not equal 1/2. A value $\theta = 1$ must not be used, because the respondent will then realize that he is telling whether or not he belongs to Group A, which is exactly what he does not wish to do. A value of θ between 1/2 and 1, for example 3/4, is usually adequate.

Example 11.5

A study is designed to estimate the proportion of people in a certain district who give false information on income tax returns. Since respondents would not admit cheating on tax returns, a random response technique is used. The experimenter constructs a deck of cards in which 3/4 of the cards are marked F, denoting a falsified return, and 1/4 are marked C, denoting a correct return. A simple random sample of $n = 400$ persons is selected from the large population of taxpayers in the district. In separate interviews each sampled taxpayer is asked to draw a card from the deck and to respond "yes" if the letter agrees with the group to which he belongs. The experiment results in $n_1 = 120$ "yes" responses. Estimate p, the proportion of taxpayers in the district who have falsified returns, and place a bound on the error of estimation.

Solution

From equation (11.14)

$$\hat{p} = \frac{\theta - 1}{2\theta - 1} + \frac{n_1}{(2\theta - 1)n}$$

$$= \frac{\frac{3}{4} - 1}{2\left(\frac{3}{4}\right) - 1} + \frac{120}{\left(2\left(\frac{3}{4}\right) - 1\right)(400)}$$

$$= -\frac{1}{2} + \frac{3}{5} = \frac{1}{10} = .1.$$

The estimated variance of $\hat{p}$ is given in equation (11.15) as

$$\hat{V}(\hat{p}) = \frac{1}{n}\left[\frac{1}{16\left(\theta - \frac{1}{2}\right)^2} - \left(\hat{p} - \frac{1}{2}\right)^2\right]$$

$$= \frac{1}{400}\left[\frac{1}{16\left(\frac{3}{4} - \frac{1}{2}\right)^2} - \left(\frac{1}{10} - \frac{1}{2}\right)^2\right]$$

$$= .0021.$$

The estimate of p with a bound on the error of estimation is then

$$\hat{p} \pm 2\sqrt{\hat{V}(\hat{p})},$$
$$.1 \pm 2\sqrt{.0021},$$

or

$$.1 \pm .092.$$

This method generally requires a very large sample size in order to obtain a reasonably small variance of the estimator. This is true because each response provides little information on the population proportion, p.

11.5   Summary

Chapter 11 presents three useful techniques for estimating population parameters when the assumptions underlying the elementary sample survey designs are not valid.

The effect of interviewer bias can be reduced by using interpenetrating subsamples. The estimator of the population mean in this case is given by equation (11.2) and the estimated variance of this estimator is given by equation (11.3).

An inadequate frame generates the problem of estimating means and totals over subpopulations. The estimator of the subpopulation mean is given by equation (11.5) and estimators of the subpopulation total are given by equations (11.8) and (11.11).

When persons being interviewed will not give correct answers to sensitive questions, a random response technique can sometimes be used. The method for estimating a population proportion, p, using this procedure is explained in Section 11.4.

References

Cochran, W. G., *Sampling Techniques*, 2d ed., New York: John Wiley and Sons, Inc., 1953.

Deming, W. E., *Sample Design in Business Research*, New York: John Wiley and Sons, Inc., 1960.

Warner, S. L., "Randomized Response: A Survey Technique for Eliminating Evasive Answer Bias," *Journal of the American Statistical Association*, **60**, 63–69, 1965.

Exercises

11.1   A researcher is interested in estimating the average yearly medical expense per family in a community of 545 families. The researcher has eight assistants available to do the field work. Skill is required to obtain accurate information on medical expenses because some respondents are reluctant to give detailed information on their health. Since the assistants differ in their interviewing abilities, the researcher decides to use 8 interpenetrating subsamples of 5 families each, with one assistant assigned to each subsample. Hence, a simple random sample of 40 families is selected and divided into 8 random subsamples. The interviews are conducted and yield the following results:

Subsample	Amount in dollars of medical expenses for past year				
1	101	95	310	427	680
2	157	192	108	960	312
3	689	432	187	512	649
4	322	48	93	162	495
5	837	649	152	175	210
6	1015	864	325	470	295
7	837	249	1127	493	218
8	327	419	291	114	287

Estimate the average medical expense per family for the past year, and place a bound on the error of estimation.

11.2   An experiment is designed to gauge the emotional reaction to a city's decision on school desegregation. A simple random sample of 50 people is interviewed and the emotional reactions are given a score from 1 to 10. The scale on which scores are assigned runs from extreme anger to extreme joy. Ten interviewers do the questioning and scoring, with each interviewer working on a random subsample (interpenetrating subsample) of 5 people. Interpenetrating subsamples are used because of the flexible nature of the scoring. The results are as follows:

Subsample	Scores				
1	5	4	6	1	8
2	4	6	5	2	7
3	9	8	9	7	5
4	8	5	4	6	3
5	6	4	5	7	9
6	1	5	6	4	7
7	6	4	3	5	2
8	5	6	7	3	4
9	2	4	4	5	3
10	9	7	8	6	4

Estimate the average score for people in the city, and place a bound on the error of estimation.

11.3   A retail store wants to estimate the average amount of all past-due accounts. The available list of past-due accounts is outdated because some accounts have since been paid. Because drawing up a new list would be expensive, the store uses the outdated list. A simple random sample of 20 accounts is selected from the list which contains 95 accounts. Of the 20 sampled accounts, 4 have been paid. The 16 past-due accounts contain the following amounts (in dollars): 3.65, 15.98, 40.70, 2.98, 50.00, 60.31, 67.21, 14.98, 10.20, 14.32, 1.87, 32.60, 19.80, 15.98, 12.20, 15.00.

Estimate the average amount of past-due accounts for the store, and place a bound on the error of estimation.

11.4   For Exercise 11.3, estimate the total amount of past-due accounts for the store, and place a bound on the error of estimation.

11.5   An employee of the store in the preceding exercise decides to look through the list of past-due accounts and mark those which have been paid. He finds that only 83 of the 95 accounts are past due. Estimate the total amount of past-due accounts using this additional information and the data of Exercise 11.3. Place a bound on the error of estimation.

11.6   A study is conducted to estimate the average number of miles from home to place of employment for household heads living in a certain suburban area. A simple random sample of 30 people is selected from the 493 heads of households in the area. While conducting interviews, the experimenter finds some household heads are not appropriate for the study because they are retired or do not go to a place of employment for various other reasons. Of the 30 sampled household heads, 24 are appropriate for the study, and the data on miles to place of employment are as follows:

$$8.5, \quad 10.2, \quad 25.1, \quad 5.0, \quad 6.3, \quad 7.9, \quad 15.8, \quad 2.1,$$
$$9.2, \quad 4.2, \quad 8.3, \quad 4.2, \quad 6.7, \quad 10.1, \quad 15.6, \quad 22.1,$$
$$10.0, \quad 6.1, \quad 7.9, \quad 1.5, \quad 8.0, \quad 11.0, \quad 20.2, \quad 9.3.$$

Estimate the average distance between home and place of employment for household heads who commute to a place of employment. Place a bound on the error of estimation.

11.7   For the data of Exercise 11.6, estimate the total travel distance between home and place of employment for all household heads in the suburban area. Place a bound on the error of estimation.

11.8   It is known that 420 out of the 493 household heads (Exercise 11.6) commute to a place of employment. Estimate the total travel distance for all household heads in the suburban area making use of this additional information. Place a bound on the error of estimation.

11.9   A public health official wants to estimate the proportion of dog owners in a city who have had their dogs vaccinated against rabies. He knows that a dog owner often gives incorrect information about rabies shots out of fear something might happen to his dog if it has not had the shots. Thus, the official decides to use a randomized response technique. He has a stack of cards with .8 of the cards marked *A* for the group having the shots, and .2 marked *B* for the group not having the shots. A simple random sample of 200 dog owners is selected. Each sampled owner is interviewed and asked to draw a card and to respond with "yes" if the letter on the card agrees with the group he is in. The official obtained 145 "yes" responses. Estimate the proportion of dog owners who have had their dogs vaccinated, and place a bound on the error of estimation. Assume that the number of dog owners in the city is very large.

11.10   A corporation executive wants to estimate the proportion of corporation
        employees who have been convicted of a misdemeanor. Since the em-
        ployees would not want to answer the question directly, the executive
        uses a randomized response technique. A simple random sample for 300
        people is selected from a large number of corporation employees. In
        separate interviews each employee draws a card from a deck which has .7
        of the cards marked "convicted" and .3 marked "not convicted." The
        employee responds "yes" if the card agrees with his category and "no"
        otherwise. The executive obtains 105 "yes" responses. Estimate the
        proportion of employees who have been convicted of a misdemeanor and
        place a bound on the error of estimation.

12 Summary

You will recall that the objective of statistics is to make inferences about a population based on information contained in a sample. This text discusses the design of sample surveys and associated methods of inference for populations containing a finite number of elements. Practical examples have been selected primarily from the fields of business and the social sciences where finite populations of human responses are frequently the target of surveys. Natural-resource management examples are also included.

The method of inference employed for most sample surveys is estimation. Thus, we consider appropriate estimators for population parameters and the associated two standard deviation bound on the error of estimation. In repeated sampling the error of estimation will be less than its bound with probability approximately equal to .95. Equivalently, we construct confidence intervals which, in repeated sampling, enclose the true population parameter approximately 95 times out of 100. The quantity of information pertinent to a given parameter is measured by the bound on the error of estimation.

The material in this text falls naturally into five segments. The first is a review of elementary concepts, the second contains useful sample survey designs, the third considers an estimator that utilizes information obtained on an auxiliary variable, the fourth gives methods of estimating the size of wildlife populations, and the fifth considers methods for making inferences when one or more of the basic assumptions associated with the standard techniques are not satisfied.

The first segment, presented in Chapters 1, 2, and 3, respectively, reviews the

217

objective of statistics and points to the peculiarities of problems arising in the social sciences, business, and natural-resource management that make them different from the traditional type of experiment conducted in the laboratory. These peculiarities primarily involve sampling from finite populations along with a number of difficulties that occur in drawing samples from human populations. The former requires modification of the formulas for the bounds on the error of estimation that one encounters in an introductory course in statistics. The difficulties associated with sampling from human populations suggest specific sample survey designs that reduce the cost of acquiring a specified quantity of information.

In Chapters 4, 5, 7, 8, and 9 we consider specific sample survey designs and their associated methods of estimation. The basic sample survey design, simple random sampling, is presented in Chapter 4. For this design, the sample is selected so that every sample of size n in the population has an equal chance of being chosen. The design does not make a specific attempt to reduce the cost of the desired quantity of information. It is the most basic type of sample survey design and all other designs are compared to it.

The second type of design, stratified random sampling, divides the population into homogeneous groups called strata. This usually produces an estimator that possesses a smaller variance than can be acquired by simple random sampling. Thus, the cost of the survey can be reduced by selecting fewer elements to achieve an equivalent bound on the error of estimation.

The third type of sample survey design is cluster sampling, which is presented in Chapters 7 and 9. Cluster sampling may reduce cost because each sampling unit is a collection of elements usually selected so as to be physically close together. Cluster sampling is most often used when a frame which lists all population elements is not available or when travel costs from element to element are considerable. Cluster sampling reduces the cost of the survey primarily by reducing the cost of collecting the data.

The fourth type of experimental design is systematic sampling which is usually applied to population elements which are available in a list or line, such as names on file cards in a drawer or people coming out of a factory. A random starting point is selected and then every kth element thereafter is sampled. Systematic sampling is frequently conducted when it is extremely costly or impossible to collect a simple random or a stratified random sample. Once again, the reduction in survey cost is primarily associated with the cost of collecting the sample.

A discussion of the ratio estimator, which utilizes information on an auxiliary variable, is covered in the third segment of material, Chapter 6. The ratio estimator illustrates how additional information, frequently acquired at little cost, can be used to reduce the variance of the estimator and, consequently, reduce the over-all cost of a survey. It also suggests the possibility of acquiring more sophisticated estimators using information on more than one auxiliary variable. This chapter on ratio estimation follows naturally the discussion on simple random sampling contained in Chapter 4. This is because one could take a measurement on y, the response of interest, for each element of the simple random sample and utilize the traditional estimators of Chapter 4. Or, as suggested in Chapter 6, we might take a measurement on both y and an auxiliary variable x for each element and utilize the additional information contributed by the auxiliary variable to acquire a better estimator of the parameter of interest. Thus, although it was not particularly stressed, ratio estimators could be employed with any of the designs discussed in the text. Because these topics are of a more advanced nature, they are omitted from the text.

Chapter 10 deals with the specific problems of estimating the size of wildlife populations. The estimators employed use recapture data, which requires that the sampling be done in at least two stages.

The fifth and final segment of material is contained in Chapter 11, which deals with three situations in which some of the basic assumptions of the standard procedures cannot be satisfied. The situations are: (1) interviewer biases, which can sometimes be minimized by using interpenetrating sub-samples, (2) an inadequate frame, which can sometimes be accounted for by using an estimator for subpopulations of the sampled population, and (3) information on sensitive questions, which can be obtained by using a randomized response model.

To summarize, we have presented various elementary sample survey designs along with their associated methods of inference. Treatment of the topics has been directed toward practical applications so that the student can see how sample survey design can be employed to make inferences at minimum cost when sampling from finite social, business, or natural-resource populations.

Appendix

Table 1   223

Table 1   Normal Curve Areas

z	.00	.01	.02	.03	.04	.05	.06	.07	.08	.09
0.0	.0000	.0040	.0080	.0120	.0160	.0199	.0239	.0279	.0319	.0359
0.1	.0398	.0438	.0478	.0517	.0557	.0596	.0636	.0675	.0714	.0753
0.2	.0793	.0832	.0871	.0910	.0948	.0987	.1026	.1064	.1103	.1141
0.3	.1179	.1217	.1255	.1293	.1331	.1368	.1406	.1443	.1480	.1517
0.4	.1554	.1591	.1628	.1664	.1700	.1736	.1772	.1808	.1844	.1879
0.5	.1915	.1950	.1985	.2019	.2054	.2088	.2123	.2157	.2190	.2224
0.6	.2257	.2291	.2324	.2357	.2389	.2422	.2454	.2486	.2517	.2549
0.7	.2580	.2611	.2642	.2673	.2704	.2734	.2764	.2794	.2823	.2852
0.8	.2881	.2910	.2939	.2967	.2995	.3023	.3051	.3078	.3106	.3133
0.9	.3159	.3186	.3212	.3238	.3264	.3289	.3315	.3340	.3365	.3389
1.0	.3413	.3438	.3461	.3485	.3508	.3531	.3554	.3577	.3599	.3621
1.1	.3643	.3665	.3686	.3708	.3729	.3749	.3770	.3790	.3810	.3830
1.2	.3849	.3869	.3888	.3907	.3925	.3944	.3962	.3980	.3997	.4015
1.3	.4032	.4049	.4066	.4082	.4099	.4115	.4131	.4147	.4162	.4177
1.4	.4192	.4207	.4222	.4236	.4251	.4265	.4279	.4292	.4306	.4319
1.5	.4332	.4345	.4357	.4370	.4382	.4394	.4406	.4418	.4429	.4441
1.6	.4452	.4463	.4474	.4484	.4495	.4505	.4515	.4525	.4535	.4545
1.7	.4554	.4564	.4573	.4582	.4591	.4599	.4608	.4616	.4625	.4633
1.8	.4641	.4649	.4656	.4664	.4671	.4678	.4686	.4693	.4699	.4706
1.9	.4713	.4719	.4726	.4732	.4738	.4744	.4750	.4756	.4761	.4767
2.0	.4772	.4778	.4783	.4788	.4793	.4798	.4803	.4808	.4812	.4817
2.1	.4821	.4826	.4830	.4834	.4838	.4842	.4846	.4850	.4854	.4857
2.2	.4861	.4864	.4868	.4871	.4875	.4878	.4881	.4884	.4887	.4890
2.3	.4893	.4896	.4898	.4901	.4904	.4906	.4909	.4911	.4913	.4916
2.4	.4918	.4920	.4922	.4925	.4927	.4929	.4931	.4932	.4934	.4936
2.5	.4938	.4940	.4941	.4943	.4945	.4946	.4948	.4949	.4951	.4952
2.6	.4953	.4955	.4956	.4957	.4959	.4960	.4961	.4962	.4963	.4964
2.7	.4965	.4966	.4967	.4968	.4969	.4970	.4971	.4972	.4973	.4974
2.8	.4974	.4975	.4976	.4977	.4977	.4978	.4979	.4979	.4980	.4981
2.9	.4981	.4982	.4982	.4982	.4984	.4984	.4985	.4985	.4986	.4986
3.0	.4987	.4987	.4987	.4988	.4988	.4989	.4989	.4989	.4990	.4990

Abridged from Table I of *Statistical Tables and Formulas* by A. Hald (New York: John Wiley & Sons, Inc., 1952). Reproduced by permission of A. Hald and the publishers, John Wiley & Sons, Inc.

Table 2 Squares and Square Roots

n	n^2	$\sqrt{n}$	$\sqrt{10n}$	n	n^2	$\sqrt{n}$	$\sqrt{10n}$
				25	625	5.000 000	15.81139
1	1	1.000 000	3.162 278	26	676	5.099 020	16.12452
2	4	1.414 214	4.472 136	27	729	5.196 152	16.43168
3	9	1.732 051	5.477 226	28	784	5.291 503	16.73320
4	16	2.000 000	6.324 555	29	841	5.385 165	17.02939
5	25	2.236 068	7.071 068	30	900	5.477 226	17.32051
6	36	2.449 490	7.745 967	31	961	5.567 764	17.60682
7	49	2.645 751	8.366 600	32	1 024	5.656 854	17.88854
8	64	2.828 427	8.944 272	33	1 089	5.744 563	18.16590
9	81	3.000 000	9.486 833	34	1 156	5.830 952	18.43909
10	100	3.162 278	10.00000	35	1 225	5.916 080	18.70829
11	121	3.316 625	10.48809	36	1 296	6.000 000	18.97367
12	144	3.464 102	10.95445	37	1 369	6.082 763	19.23538
13	169	3.605 551	11.40175	38	1 444	6.164 414	19.49359
14	196	3.741 657	11.83216	39	1 521	6.244 998	19.74842
15	225	3.872 983	12.24745	40	1 600	6.324 555	20.00000
16	256	4.000 000	12.64911	41	1 681	6.403 124	20.24846
17	289	4.123 106	13.03840	42	1 764	6.480 741	20.49390
18	324	4.242 641	13.41641	43	1 849	6.557 439	20.73644
19	361	4.358 899	13.78405	44	1 936	6.633 250	20.97618
20	400	4.472 136	14.14214	45	2 025	6.708 204	21.21320
21	441	4.582 576	14.49138	46	2 116	6.782 330	21.44761
22	484	4.690 416	14.83240	47	2 209	6.855 655	21.67948
23	529	4.795 832	15.16575	48	2 304	6.928 203	21.90890
24	576	4.898 979	15.49193	49	2 401	7.000 000	22.13594

From *Handbook of Tables for Probability and Statistics*, Second Edition, edited by William H. Beyer (Cleveland: The Chemical Rubber Company, 1968.) Reproduced by permission of the publishers, The Chemical Rubber Company.

Table 2   225

n	n^2	$\sqrt{n}$	$\sqrt{10n}$	n	n^2	$\sqrt{n}$	$\sqrt{10n}$
50	2 500	7.071 068	22.36068	90	8 100	9.486 833	30.00000
51	2 601	7.141 428	22.58318	91	8 281	9.539 392	30.16621
52	2 704	7.211 103	22.80351	92	8 464	9.591 663	30.33150
53	2 809	7.280 110	23.02173	93	8 649	9.643 651	30.49590
54	2 916	7.348 469	23.23790	94	8 836	9.695 360	30.65942
55	3 025	7.416 198	23.45208	95	9 025	9.746 794	30.82207
56	3 136	7.483 315	23.66432	96	9 216	9.797 959	30.98387
57	3 249	7.549 834	23.87467	97	9 409	9.848 858	31.14482
58	3 364	7.615 773	24.08319	98	9 604	9.899 495	31.30495
59	3 481	7.681 146	24.28992	99	9 801	9.949 874	31.46427
60	3 600	7.745 967	24.49490	100	10 000	10.00000	31.62278
61	3 721	7.810 250	24.69818	101	10 201	10.04988	31.78050
62	3 844	7.874 008	24.89980	102	10 404	10.09950	31.93744
63	3 969	7.937 254	25.09980	103	10 609	10.14889	32.09361
64	4 096	8.000 000	25.29822	104	10 816	10.19804	32.24903
65	4 225	8.062 258	25.49510	105	11 025	10.24695	32.40370
66	4 356	8.124 038	25.69047	106	11 236	10.29563	32.55764
67	4 489	8.185 353	25.88436	107	11 449	10.34408	32.71085
68	4 624	8.246 211	26.07681	108	11 664	10.39230	32.86335
69	4 761	8.306 624	26.26785	109	11 881	10.44031	33.01515
70	4 900	8.366 600	26.45751	110	12 100	10.48809	33.16625
71	5 041	8.426 150	26.64583	111	12 321	10.53565	33.31666
72	5 184	8.485 281	26.83282	112	12 544	10.58301	33.46640
73	5 329	8.544 004	27.01851	113	12 769	10.63015	33.61547
74	5 476	8.602 325	27.20294	114	12 996	10.67708	33.76389
75	5 625	8.660 254	27.38613	115	13 225	10.72381	33.91165
76	5 776	8.717 798	27.56810	116	13 456	10.77033	34.05877
77	5 929	8.774 964	27.74887	117	13 689	10.81665	34.20526
78	6 084	8.831 761	27.92848	118	13 924	10.86278	34.35113
79	6 241	8.888 194	28.10694	119	14 161	10.90871	34.49638
80	6 400	8.944 272	28.28427	120	14 400	10.95445	34.64102
81	6 561	9.000 000	28.46050	121	14 641	11.00000	34.78505
82	6 724	9.055 385	28.63564	122	14 884	11.04536	34.92850
83	6 889	9.110 434	28.80972	123	15 129	11.09054	35.07136
84	7 056	9.165 151	28.98275	124	15 376	11.13553	35.21363
85	7 225	9.219 544	29.15476	125	15 625	11.18034	35.35534
86	7 396	9.273 618	29.32576	126	15 876	11.22497	35.49648
87	7 569	9.327 379	29.49576	127	16 129	11.26943	35.63706
88	7 744	9.380 832	29.66479	128	16 384	11.31371	35.77709
89	7 921	9.433 981	29.83287	129	16 641	11.35782	35.91657

Table 2

n	n^2	$\sqrt{n}$	$\sqrt{10n}$	n	n^2	$\sqrt{n}$	$\sqrt{10n}$
130	16 900	11.40175	36.05551	170	28 900	13.03840	41.23106
131	17 161	11.44552	36.19392	171	29 241	13.07670	41.35215
132	17 424	11.48913	36.33180	172	29 584	13.11488	41.47288
133	17 689	11.53256	36.46917	173	29 929	13.15295	41.59327
134	17 956	11.57584	36.60601	174	30 276	13.19091	41.71331
135	18 225	11.61895	36.74235	175	30 625	13.22876	41.83300
136	18 496	11.66190	36.87818	176	30 976	13.26650	41.95235
137	18 769	11.70470	37.01351	177	31 329	13.30413	42.07137
138	19 044	11.74734	37.14835	178	31 684	13.34166	42.19005
139	19 321	11.78983	37.28270	179	32 041	13.37909	42.30839
140	19 600	11.83216	37.41657	180	32 400	13.41641	42.42641
141	19 881	11.87434	37.54997	181	32 761	13.45362	42.54409
142	20 164	11.91638	37.68289	182	33 124	13.49074	42.66146
143	20 449	11.95826	37.81534	183	33 489	13.52775	42.77850
144	20 736	12.00000	37.94733	184	33 856	13.56466	42.89522
145	21 025	12.04159	38.07887	185	34 225	13.60147	43.01163
146	21 316	12.08305	38.20995	186	34 596	13.63818	43.12772
147	21 609	12.12436	38.34058	187	34 969	13.67479	43.24350
148	21 904	12.16553	38.47077	188	35 344	13.71131	43.35897
149	22 201	12.20656	38.60052	189	35 721	13.74773	43.47413
150	22 500	12.24745	38.72983	190	36 100	13.78405	43.58899
151	22 801	12.28821	38.85872	191	36 481	13.82027	43.70355
152	23 104	12.32883	38.98718	192	36 864	13.85641	43.81780
153	23 409	12.36932	39.11521	193	37 249	13.89244	43.93177
154	23 716	12.40967	39.24283	194	37 636	13.92839	44.04543
155	24 025	12.44990	39.37004	195	38 025	13.96424	44.15880
156	24 336	12.49000	39.49684	196	38 416	14.00000	44.27189
157	24 649	12.52996	39.62323	197	38 809	14.03567	44.38468
158	24 964	12.56981	39.74921	198	39 204	14.07125	44.49719
159	25 281	12.60952	39.87480	199	39 601	14.10674	44.60942
160	25 600	12.64911	40.00000	200	40 000	14.14214	44.72136
161	25 921	12.68858	40.12481	201	40 401	14.17745	44.83302
162	26 244	12.72792	40.24922	202	40 804	14.21267	44.94441
163	26 569	12.76715	40.37326	203	41 209	14.24781	45.05552
164	26 896	12.80625	40.49691	204	41 616	14.28286	45.16636
165	27 225	12.84523	40.62019	205	42 025	14.31782	45.27693
166	27 556	12.88410	40.74310	206	42 436	14.35270	45.38722
167	27 889	12.92285	40.86563	207	42 849	14.38749	45.49725
168	28 224	12.96148	40.98780	208	43 264	14.42221	45.60702
169	28 561	13.00000	41.10961	209	43 681	14.45683	45.71652

Table 2   227

n	n^2	$\sqrt{n}$	$\sqrt{10n}$	n	n^2	$\sqrt{n}$	$\sqrt{10n}$
210	44 100	14.49138	45.82576	250	62 500	15.81139	50.00000
211	44 521	14.52584	45.93474	251	63 001	15.84298	50.09990
212	44 944	14.56022	46.04346	252	63 504	15.87451	50.19960
213	45 369	14.59452	46.15192	253	64 009	15.90597	50.29911
214	45 796	14.62874	46.26013	254	64 516	15.93738	50.39841
215	46 225	14.66288	46.36809	255	65 025	15.96872	50.49752
216	46 656	14.69694	46.47580	256	65 536	16.00000	50.59644
217	47 089	14.73092	46.58326	257	66 049	16.03122	50.69517
218	47 524	14.76482	46.69047	258	66 564	16.06238	50.79370
219	47 961	14.79865	46.79744	259	67 081	16.09348	50.89204
220	48 400	14.83240	46.90416	260	67 600	16.12452	50.99020
221	48 841	14.86607	47.01064	261	68 121	16.15549	51.08816
222	49 284	14.89966	47.11688	262	68 644	16.18641	51.18594
223	49 729	14.93318	47.22288	263	69 169	16.21727	51.28353
224	50 176	14.96663	47.32864	264	69 696	16.24808	51.38093
225	50 625	15.00000	47.43416	265	70 225	16.27882	51.47815
226	51 076	15.03330	47.53946	266	70 756	16.30951	51.57519
227	51 529	15.06652	47.64452	267	71 289	16.34013	51.67204
228	51 984	15.09967	47.74935	268	71 824	16.37071	51.76872
229	52 441	15.13275	47.85394	269	72 361	16.40122	51.86521
230	52 900	15.16575	47.95832	270	72 900	16.43168	51.96152
231	53 361	15.19868	48.06246	271	73 441	16.46208	52.05766
232	53 824	15.23155	48.16638	272	73 984	16.49242	52.15362
233	54 289	15.26434	48.27007	273	74 529	16.52271	52.24940
234	54 756	15.29706	48.37355	274	75 076	16.55295	52.34501
235	55 225	15.32971	48.47680	275	75 625	16.58312	52.44044
236	55 696	15.36229	48.57983	276	76 176	16.61325	52.53570
237	56 169	15.39480	48.68265	277	76 729	16.64332	52.63079
238	56 644	15.42725	48.78524	278	77 284	16.67333	52.72571
239	57 121	15.45962	48.88763	279	77 841	16.70329	52.82045
240	57 600	15.49193	48.98979	280	78 400	16.73320	52.91503
241	58 081	15.52417	49.09175	281	78 961	16.76305	53.00943
242	58 564	15.55635	49.19350	282	79 524	16.79286	53.10367
243	59 049	15.58846	49.29503	283	80 089	16.82260	53.19774
244	59 536	15.62050	49.39636	284	80 656	16.85230	53.29165
245	60 025	15.65248	49.49747	285	81 225	16.88194	53.38539
246	60 516	15.68439	49.59839	286	81 796	16.91153	53.47897
247	61 009	15.71623	49.69909	287	82 369	16.94107	53.57238
248	61 504	15.74802	49.79960	288	82 944	16.97056	53.66563
249	62 001	15.77973	49.89990	289	83 521	17.00000	53.75872

n	n^2	$\sqrt{n}$	$\sqrt{10n}$	n	n^2	$\sqrt{n}$	$\sqrt{10n}$
290	84 100	17.02939	53.85165	330	108 900	18.16590	57.44563
291	84 681	17.05872	53.94442	331	109 561	18.19341	57.53260
292	85 264	17.08801	54.03702	332	110 224	18.22087	57.61944
293	85 849	17.11724	54.12947	333	110 889	18.24829	57.70615
294	86 436	17.14643	54.22177	334	111 556	18.27567	57.79273
295	87 025	17.17556	54.31390	335	112 225	18.30301	57.87918
296	87 616	17.20465	54.40588	336	112 896	18.33030	57.96551
297	88 209	17.23369	54.49771	337	113 569	18.35756	58.05170
298	88 804	17.26268	54.58938	338	114 244	18.38478	58.13777
299	89 401	17.29162	54.68089	339	114 921	18.41195	58.22371
300	90 000	17.32051	54.77226	340	115 600	18.43909	58.30952
301	90 601	17.34935	54.86347	341	116 281	18.46619	58.39521
302	91 204	17.37815	54.95453	342	116 964	18.49324	58.48077
303	91 809	17.40690	55.04544	343	117 649	18.52026	58.56620
304	92 416	17.43560	55.13620	344	118 336	18.54724	58.65151
305	93 025	17.46425	55.22681	345	119 025	18.57418	58.73670
306	93 636	17.49286	55.31727	346	119 716	18.60108	58.82176
307	94 249	17.52142	55.40758	347	120 409	18.62794	58.90671
308	94 864	17.54993	55.49775	348	121 104	18.65476	58.99152
309	95 481	17.57840	55.58777	349	121 801	18.68154	59.07622
310	96 100	17.60682	55.67764	350	122 500	18.70829	59.16080
311	96 721	17.63519	55.76737	351	123 201	18.73499	59.24525
312	97 344	17.66352	55.85696	352	123 904	18.76166	59.32959
313	97 969	17.69181	55.94640	353	124 609	18.78829	59.41380
314	98 596	17.72005	56.03570	354	125 316	18.81489	59.40790
315	99 225	17.74824	56.12486	355	126 025	18.84144	59.58188
316	99 856	17.77639	56.21388	356	126 736	18.86796	59.66574
317	100 489	17.80449	56.30275	357	127 449	18.89444	59.74948
318	101 124	17.83255	56.39149	358	128 164	18.92089	59.83310
319	101 761	17.86057	56.48008	359	128 881	18.94730	59.91661
320	102 400	17.88854	56.56854	360	129 600	18.97367	60.00000
321	103 041	17.91647	56.65686	361	130 321	19.00000	60.08328
322	103 684	17.94436	56.74504	362	131 044	19.02630	60.16644
323	104 329	17.97220	56.83309	363	131 769	19.05256	60.24948
324	104 976	18.00000	56.92100	364	132 496	19.07878	60.33241
325	105 625	18.02776	57.00877	365	133 225	19.10497	60.41523
326	106 276	18.05547	57.09641	366	133 956	19.13113	60.49793
327	106 929	18.08314	57.18391	367	134 689	19.15724	60.58052
328	107 584	18.11077	57.27128	368	135 424	19.18333	60.66300
329	108 241	18.13836	57.35852	369	136 161	19.20937	60.74537

Table 2   229

n	n^2	$\sqrt{n}$	$\sqrt{10n}$	n	n^2	$\sqrt{n}$	$\sqrt{10n}$
370	136 900	19.23538	60.82763	410	168 100	20.24846	64.03124
371	137 641	19.26136	60.90977	411	168 921	20.27313	64.10928
372	138 384	19.28730	60.99180	412	169 744	20.29778	64.18723
373	139 129	19.31321	61.07373	413	170 569	20.32240	64.26508
374	139 876	19.33908	61.15554	414	171 396	20.34699	64.34283
375	140 625	19.36492	61.23724	415	172 225	20.37155	64.42049
376	141 376	19.39072	61.31884	416	173 056	20.39608	64.49806
377	142 129	19.41649	61.40033	417	173 889	20.42058	64.57554
378	142 184	19.44222	61.48170	418	174 724	20.44505	64.65292
379	143 641	19.46792	61.56298	419	175 561	20.46949	64.73021
380	144 400	19.49359	61.64414	420	176 400	20.49390	64.80741
381	145 161	19.51922	61.72520	421	177 241	20.51828	64.88451
382	145 924	19.54482	61.80615	422	178 084	20.54264	64.96153
383	146 689	19.57039	61.88699	423	178 929	20.56696	65.03845
384	147 456	19.59592	61.96773	424	179 776	20.59126	65.11528
385	148 225	19.62142	62.04837	425	180 625	20.61553	65.19202
386	148 996	19.64688	62.12890	426	181 476	20.63977	65.26868
387	149 769	19.67232	62.20932	427	182 329	20.66398	65.34524
388	150 544	19.69772	62.28965	428	183 184	20.68816	65.42171
389	151 321	19.72308	62.36986	429	184 041	20.71232	65.49809
390	152 100	19.74842	62.44998	430	184 900	20.73644	65.57439
391	152 881	19.77372	62.52999	431	185 761	20.76054	65.65059
392	153 664	19.79899	62.60990	432	186 624	20.78461	65.72671
393	154 449	19.82423	62.68971	433	187 489	20.80865	65.80274
394	155 236	19.84943	62.76942	434	188 356	20.83267	65.87868
395	156 025	19.87461	62.84903	435	189 225	20.85665	65.95453
396	156 816	19.89975	62.92853	436	190 096	20.88061	66.03030
397	157 609	19.92486	63.00794	437	190 969	20.90454	66.10598
398	158 404	19.94994	63.08724	438	191 844	20.92845	66.18157
399	159 201	19.97498	63.16645	439	192 721	20.95233	66.25708
400	160 000	20.00000	63.24555	440	193 600	20.97618	66.33250
401	160 801	20.02498	63.32456	441	194 481	21.00000	66.40783
402	161 604	20.04994	63.40347	442	195 224	21.02380	66.48308
403	162 409	20.07486	63.48228	443	196 249	21.04757	66.55825
404	163 216	20.09975	63.56099	444	197 136	21.07131	66.63332
405	164 025	20.12461	63.63961	445	198 025	21.09502	66.70832
406	164 836	20.14944	63.71813	446	198 916	21.11871	66.78323
407	165 649	20.17424	63.79655	447	199·809	21.14237	66.85806
408	166 464	20.19901	63.87488	448	200 704	21.16601	66.93280
409	167 281	20.22375	63.95311	449	201 601	21.18962	67.00746

Table 2

n	n^2	$\sqrt{n}$	$\sqrt{10n}$	n	n^2	$\sqrt{n}$	$\sqrt{10n}$
450	202 500	21.21320	67.08204	490	240 100	22.13594	70.00000
451	203 401	21.23676	67.15653	491	241 081	22.15852	70.07139
452	204 304	21.26029	67.23095	492	242 064	22.18107	70.14271
453	205 209	21.28380	67.30527	493	243 049	22.20360	70.21396
454	206 116	21.30728	67.37952	494	244 036	22.22611	70.28513
455	207 025	21.33073	67.45369	495	245 025	22.24860	70.35624
456	207 936	21.35416	67.52777	496	246 016	22.27106	70.42727
457	208 849	21.37756	67.60178	497	247 009	22.29350	70.49823
458	209 764	21.40093	67.67570	498	248 004	22.31591	70.56912
459	210 681	21.42429	67.74954	499	249 001	22.33831	70.63993
460	211 600	21.44761	67.82330	500	250 000	22.36068	70.71068
461	212 521	21.47091	67.89698	50!	251 001	22.38303	70.78135
462	213 444	21.49419	67.97058	502	252 004	22.40536	70.85196
463	214 369	21.51743	68.04410	503	253 009	22.42766	70.92249
464	215 296	21.54066	68.11755	504	254 016	22.44994	70.99296
465	216 225	21.56386	68.19091	505	255 025	22.47221	71.06335
466	217 156	21.58703	68.26419	506	256 036	22.49444	71.13368
467	218 089	21.61018	68.33740	507	257 049	22.51666	71.20393
468	219 024	21.63331	68.41053	508	258 064	22.53886	71.27412
469	219 961	21.45641	68.48357	509	259 081	22.56103	71.34424
470	220 900	21.67948	68.55655	510	260 100	22.58318	71.41428
471	221 841	21.70253	68.62944	511	261 121	22.60531	71.48426
472	222 784	21.72556	68.70226	512	262 144	22.62742	71.55418
473	223 729	21.74856	68.77500	513	263 169	22.64950	71.62402
474	224 676	21.77154	68.84766	514	264 196	22.67157	71.69379
475	225 625	21.79449	68.92024	515	265 225	22.69861	71.76350
476	226 576	21.81742	68.99275	516	266 256	22.71563	71.83314
477	227 529	21.84033	69.06519	517	267 289	22.73763	71.90271
478	228 484	21.86321	69.13754	518	268 324	22.75961	71.97222
479	229 441	21.88607	69.20983	519	269 361	22.78157	72.04165
480	230 400	21.90890	69.28203	520	270 400	22.80351	72.11103
481	213 361	21.93171	69.35416	521	271 441	22.82542	72.18033
482	232 324	21.95450	69.42622	522	272 484	22.84732	72.24957
483	233 289	21.97726	69.49820	523	273 529	22.86919	72.31874
484	234 256	22.00000	69.57011	524	274 576	22.89105	72.38784
485	235 225	22.02272	69.64194	525	275 625	22.91288	72.45688
486	236 196	22.04541	69.71370	526	276 676	22.93469	72.52586
487	237 169	22.06808	69.78539	527	277 729	22.95648	72.59477
488	238 144	22.09072	69.85700	528	278 784	22.97825	72.66361
489	239 121	22.11334	69.92853	529	279 841	23.00000	72.73239

Table 2   231

n	n^2	$\sqrt{n}$	$\sqrt{10n}$	n	n^2	$\sqrt{n}$	$\sqrt{10n}$
530	280 900	23.02173	72.80110	570	324 900	23.87467	75.49834
531	281 961	23.04344	72.86075	571	326 041	23.89561	75.56454
532	283 024	23.06513	72.93833	572	327 184	23.91652	75.63068
533	284 089	23.08679	73.00685	573	328 329	23.93742	75.69676
534	185 156	23.10844	73.07530	574	329 476	23.95830	75.76279
535	286 225	23.13007	73.14369	575	330 625	23.97916	75.82875
536	287 296	23.15167	73.21202	576	331 776	24.00000	75.89466
537	288 369	23.17326	73.28028	577	332 929	24.02082	75.96052
538	289 444	23.19483	73.34848	578	334 084	24.04163	76.02631
539	290 521	23.21637	73.41662	579	335 241	24.06242	76.09205
540	291 600	23.23790	73.48469	580	336 400	24.08319	76.15773
541	292 681	23.25941	73.55270	581	337 561	24.10394	76.22336
542	293 764	23.28089	73.62065	582	338 724	24.12468	76.28892
543	294 849	23.30236	73.68853	583	339 889	24.14539	76.35444
544	295 936	23.32381	73.75636	584	341 056	24.16609	76.41989
545	297 025	23.34524	73.82412	585	342 225	24.18677	76.48529
546	298 116	23.36664	73.89181	586	343 396	24.20744	76.55064
547	299 209	23.38803	73.95945	587	344 569	24.22808	76.61593
548	300 304	23.40940	74.02702	588	345 744	24.24871	76.68116
549	301 401	23.43075	74.09453	589	346 921	24.26932	76.74634
550	302 500	23.45208	74.16198	590	348 100	24.28992	76.81146
551	303 601	23.47339	74.22937	591	349 281	24.31049	76.87652
552	304 704	23.49468	74.29670	592	350 464	24.33105	76.94154
553	305 809	23.51595	74.36397	593	351 649	24.35159	77.00649
554	306 916	23.53720	74.43118	594	352 836	24.37212	77.07140
555	308 025	23.55844	74.49832	595	354 025	24.39262	77.13624
556	309 136	23.57965	74.56541	596	355 216	24.41311	77.20104
557	310 249	23.60085	74.63243	597	356 409	24.43358	77.26578
558	311 364	23.62202	74.69940	598	357 604	24.45404	77.33046
559	312 481	23.64318	74.76630	599	358 801	24.47448	77.39509
560	313 600	23.66432	74.83315	600	360 000	24.49490	77.45967
561	314 721	23.68544	74.89993	601	361 201	24.51530	77.52419
562	315 844	23.70654	74.96666	602	362 404	24.53569	77.58866
563	316 969	23.72762	75.03333	603	363 609	24.55606	77.65307
564	318 096	23.74868	75.09993	604	364 816	24.57641	77.71744
565	319 225	23.76973	75.16648	605	366 025	24.59675	77.78175
566	320 356	23.79075	75.23297	606	367 236	24.61707	77.84600
567	321 489	23.81176	75.29940	607	368 449	24.63737	77.91020
568	322 624	23.83275	75.36577	608	369 664	24.65766	77.97435
569	323 761	23.85372	75.43209	609	370 881	24.67793	78.03845

Table 2

n	n^2	$\sqrt{n}$	$\sqrt{10n}$	n	n^2	$\sqrt{n}$	$\sqrt{10n}$
610	372 100	24.69818	78.10250	650	422 500	25.49510	80.62258
611	373 321	24.71841	78.16649	651	423 801	25.51470	80.68457
612	374 544	24.73863	78.23043	652	425 104	25.53429	80.74652
613	375 769	24.75884	78.29432	653	426 409	25.55386	80.80842
614	376 996	24.77902	78.35815	654	427 716	25.57342	80.87027
615	378 225	24.79919	78.42194	655	429 025	25.59297	80.93207
616	379 456	24.81935	78.48567	656	430 336	25.61250	80.00383
617	380 689	24.83948	78.54935	657	431 649	25.63201	81.05554
618	381 924	24.85961	78.61298	658	432 964	25.65151	81.11720
619	383· 161	24.87971	78.67655	659	434 281	35.67100	81.17881
620	384 400	24.89980	78.74008	660	435 600	25.69047	81.24038
621	385 641	24.91987	78.80355	661	436 921	25.70992	81.30191
622	386 884	24.93993	78.86698	662	438 244	25.72936	81.36338
623	388 129	24.95997	78.93035	663	439 569	25.74879	81.42481
624	389 376	24.97999	78.99367	664	440 896	25.76820	81.48620
625	390 625	25.00000	79.05694	665	442 225	25.78759	81.54753
626	391 876	25.01999	79.12016	666	443 556	25.80698	81.60882
627	393 129	25.03997	79.18333	667	444 889	25.82634	81.67007
628	394 384	25.05993	79.24645	668	446 224	25.84570	81.73127
629	395 641	25.07987	79.30952	669	447 561	25.86503	81.79242
630	396 900	25.09980	79.37254	670	448 900	25.88436	81.85353
631	398 161	25.11971	79.43551	671	450 241	25.90367	81.91459
632	399 424	25.13961	79.49843	672	451 584	25.92296	81.97561
633	400 689	25.15949	79.56130	673	452 929	25.94224	82.03658
634	401 956	25.17936	79.62412	674	454 276	25.96151	82.09750
635	403 225	25.19921	79.68689	675	455 625	25.98076	82.15838
636	404 496	25.21904	79.74961	676	456 976	26.00000	82.21922
637	405 769	25.23886	79.81228	677	458 329	26.01922	82.28001
638	407 044	25.25866	79.87490	678	459 684	26.03843	82.34076
639	408 321	25.27845	79.93748	679	461 041	26.05763	82.40146
640	409 600	25.29822	80.00000	680	462 400	26.07681	82.46211
641	410 881	25.31798	80.06248	681	463 761	26.09598	82.52272
642	412 164	25.33772	80.12490	682	465 124	26.11513	82.58329
643	413 449	25.35744	80.18728	683	466 489	26.13427	82.64381
644	414 736	25.37716	80.24961	684	467 856	26.15339	82.70429
645	416 025	25.39685	80.31189	685	469 225	26.17250	82.76473
646	417 316	25.41653	80.37413	686	470 596	26.19160	82.82512
647	418 609	25.43619	80.43631	687	471 969	26.21068	82.88546
648	419 904	25.45584	80.49845	688	473 344	26.22975	82.94577
649	421 201	25.47548	80.56054	689	474 721	26.24881	83.00602

Table 2   233

n	n^2	$\sqrt{n}$	$\sqrt{10n}$	n	n^2	$\sqrt{n}$	$\sqrt{10n}$
690	476 100	26.26785	83.06624	730	532 900	27.01851	85.44004
691	477 481	26.28688	83.12641	731	534 361	27.03701	85.49854
692	478 864	26.30589	83.18654	732	535 824	27.05550	85.55700
693	480 249	26.32489	83.24662	733	537 289	27.07397	85.61542
694	481 636	26.34388	83.30666	734	538 756	27.09243	85.67380
695	483 025	26.36285	83.36666	735	540 225	27.11088	85.73214
696	484 416	26.38181	83.42661	736	541 696	27.12932	85.79044
697	485 809	26.40076	83.48653	737	543 169	27.14774	85.84870
698	487 204	26.41969	83.54639	738	544 644	27.16616	85.90693
699	488 601	26.43861	83.60622	739	546 121	27.18455	85.96511
700	490 000	26.45751	83.66600	740	547 600	27.20294	86.02325
701	491 401	26.47640	83.72574	741	549 081	27.22132	86.08136
702	492 804	26.49528	83.78544	742	550 564	27.23968	86.13942
703	494 209	26.51415	83.84510	743	552 049	27.25803	86.19745
704	495 616	26.53300	83.90471	744	553 536	27.27636	86.25543
705	497 025	26.55184	83.96428	745	555 025	27.29469	86.31338
706	498 436	26.57066	84.02381	746	556 516	27.31300	86.37129
707	499 849	26.58947	84.08329	747	558 009	27.33130	86.42916
708	501 264	26.60827	84.14274	748	559 504	27.34959	86.48699
709	502 681	26.62705	84.20214	749	561 001	27.36786	86.54479
710	504 100	26.64583	84.26150	750	562 500	27.38613	86.60254
711	505 521	26.66458	84.32082	751	564 001	27.40438	86.66026
712	506 944	26.68333	84.38009	752	565 504	27.42262	86.71793
713	508 369	26.70206	84.43933	753	567 009	27.44085	86.77557
714	509 796	26.72078	84.49852	754	568 516	27.45906	86.83317
715	511 225	26.73948	84.55767	755	570 025	27.47726	86.89074
716	512 656	26.75818	84.61678	756	571 536	27.49545	86.94826
717	514 089	26.77686	84.67585	757	573 049	27.51363	87.00575
718	515 524	26.79552	84.73488	758	574 564	27.53180	87.06320
719	516 961	26.81418	84.79387	759	576 081	27.54995	87.12061
720	518 400	26.83282	84.85281	760	577 600	27.56810	87.17798
721	519 841	26.85144	84.91172	761	579 121	27.58623	87.23531
722	521 284	26.87006	84.97058	762	580 644	27.60435	87.29261
723	522 729	26.88866	85.02941	763	582 169	27.62245	87.34987
724	524 176	26.90725	85.08819	764	583 696	27.64055	87.40709
725	525 625	26.92582	85.14693	765	585 225	27.65863	87.46428
726	527 076	26.94439	85.20563	766	586 756	27.67671	87.52143
727	528 529	26.96294	85.26429	767	588 289	27.69476	87.57854
728	529 984	26.98148	85.32292	768	589 824	27.71281	87.63561
729	531 441	27.00000	85.38150	769	591 361	27.73085	87.69265

Table 2

n	n^2	$\sqrt{n}$	$\sqrt{10n}$	n	n^2	$\sqrt{n}$	$\sqrt{10n}$
770	592 900	27.74887	87.74964	810	656 100	28.46050	90.00000
771	594 441	27.76689	87.80661	811	657 721	28.47806	90.05554
772	595 984	27.78489	87.86353	812	659 344	28.49561	90.11104
773	597 529	27.80288	87.92042	813	660 969	28.51315	90.16651
774	599 076	27.82086	87.97727	814	662 596	28.53069	90.22195
775	600 625	27.83882	88.03408	815	664 225	28.54820	90.27735
776	602 176	27.85678	88.09086	816	665 856	28.56571	90.33272
777	603 729	27.87472	88.14760	817	667 489	28.58321	90.38805
778	605 284	27.89265	88.20431	818	669 124	28.60070	90.44335
779	606 841	27.91057	88.26098	819	670 761	28.61818	90.49862
780	608 400	27.92848	88.31761	820	672 400	28.63564	90.55385
781	609 961	27.94638	88.37420	821	674 041	28.65310	90.60905
782	611 524	27.96426	88.43076	822	675 684	28.67054	90.66422
783	613 089	27.98214	88.48729	823	677 329	28.68798	90.71935
784	614 656	28.00000	88.54377	824	678 976	28.70540	90.77445
785	616 225	28.01785	88.60023	825	680 625	28.72281	90.82951
786	617 796	28.03569	88.65664	826	682 276	28.74022	90.88354
787	619 369	28.05352	88.71302	827	683 929	28.75761	90.93954
788	620 944	28.07134	88.76936	828	685 584	28.77499	90.99451
789	622 521	28.08914	88.82567	829	687 241	28.79236	91.04944
790	624 100	28.10694	88.88194	830	688 900	28.80972	91.10434
791	625 681	28.12472	88.93818	831	690 561	28.82707	91.15920
792	627 264	28.14249	88.99438	832	692 224	28.84441	91.21403
793	628 849	28.16026	89.05055	833	693 889	28.86174	91.26883
794	630 436	28.17801	89.10668	834	695 556	28.87906	91.32360
795	632 025	28.19574	89.16277	835	697 225	28.89637	91.37833
796	633 616	28.21347	89.21883	836	698 896	28.91366	91.43304
797	635 209	28.23119	89.27486	837	700 569	28.93095	91.48770
798	636 804	28.24889	89.33085	838	702 244	28.94823	91.54234
799	638 401	28.26659	89.38680	839	703 921	28.96550	91.59694
800	640 000	28.28427	89.44272	840	705 600	28.98275	91.65151
801	641 601	28.30194	89.49860	841	707 281	29.00000	91.70605
802	643 204	28.31960	89.55445	842	708 964	29.01724	91.76056
803	644 809	28.33725	89.61027	843	710 649	29.03446	91.81503
804	646 416	28.35489	89.66605	844	712 336	29.05168	91.86947
805	648 025	28.37252	89.72179	345	714 025	29.06888	91.92388
806	649 636	28.39014	89.77750	846	715 716	29.08608	91.97826
807	651 249	28.40775	89.83318	847	717 409	29.10326	92.03260
808	652 864	28.42534	89.88882	848	719 104	29.12044	92.08692
809	654 481	28.44293	89.94443	849	720 801	29.13760	92.14120

Table 2   235

n	n^2	$\sqrt{n}$	$\sqrt{10n}$	n	n^2	$\sqrt{n}$	$\sqrt{10n}$
850	722 500	29.15476	92.19544	890	792 100	29.83287	94.33981
851	724 201	29.17190	92.24966	891	793 881	29.84962	94.39280
852	725 904	29.18904	92.30385	892	795 664	29.86637	94.44575
853	727 609	29.20616	92.35800	893	797 449	29.88311	94.49868
854	729 316	29.22328	92.41212	894	799 236	29.89983	94.55157
855	731 025	29.24038	92.46621	895	801 025	29.91655	94.60444
856	732 736	29.25748	92.52027	896	802 816	29.93326	94.65728
857	734 449	29.27456	92.57429	897	804 609	29.94996	94.71008
858	736 164	29.29164	92.62829	898	806 404	29.96665	94.76286
859	737 881	29.30870	92.68225	899	808 201	29.98333	94.81561
860	739 600	29.32576	92.73618	900	810 000	30.00000	94.86833
861	741 321	29.34280	92.79009	901	811 801	30.01666	94.92102
862	743 044	29.35984	92.84396	902	813 604	30.03331	94.97368
863	744 769	29.37686	92.89779	903	815 409	30.04996	95.02631
864	746 496	29.39388	92.95160	904	817 216	30.06659	95.07891
865	748 225	29.41088	93.00538	905	819 025	30.08322	95.13149
866	749 956	29.42788	93.05912	906	820 836	30.09983	95.18403
867	751 689	29.44486	93.11283	907	822 649	30.11644	95.23655
868	753 424	29.46184	93.16652	908	824 464	30.13304	95.28903
869	755 161	29.47881	93.22017	909	826 281	30.14963	95.34149
870	756 900	29.49576	93.27379	910	828 100	30.16621	95.39392
871	758 641	29.51271	93.32738	911	829 921	30.18278	95.44632
872	760 384	29.52965	93.38094	912	831 744	30.19934	95.49869
873	762 129	29.54657	93.43447	913	833 569	30.21589	95.55103
874	763 876	29.56349	93.48797	914	835 396	30.23243	95.60335
875	765 625	29.58040	93.54143	915	837 225	30.24897	95.65563
876	767 376	29.59730	93.59487	916	839 056	30.26549	95.70789
877	769 129	29.61419	93.64828	917	840 889	30.28201	95.76012
878	770 884	29.63106	93.70165	918	842 724	30.29851	95.81232
879	772 641	29.64793	93.75500	919	844 561	30.31501	95.86449
880	774 400	29.66479	93.80832	920	846 400	30.33150	95.91663
881	776 161	29.68164	93.86160	921	848 241	30.34798	95.96874
882	777 924	29.69848	93.91486	922	850 084	30.36445	96.02083
883	779 689	29.71532	93.96808	923	851 929	30.38092	96.07289
884	781 456	29.73214	94.02127	924	853 776	30.39737	96.12492
885	783 225	29.74895	94.07444	925	855 625	30.41381	96.17692
886	784 996	29.76575	94.12757	926	857 476	30.43025	96.22889
887	786 769	29.78255	94.18068	927	859 329	30.44667	96.28084
888	788 544	29.79933	94.23375	928	861 184	30.46309	96.33276
889	790 321	29.81610	94.28680	929	863 041	30.47950	96.38465

n	n^2	$\sqrt{n}$	$\sqrt{10n}$	n	n^2	$\sqrt{n}$	$\sqrt{10n}$
930	864 900	30.49590	96.43651	965	931 225	31.06445	98.23441
931	866 761	30.51229	96.48834	966	933 156	31.08054	98.28530
932	868 624	30.52868	96.54015	967	935 089	31.09662	98.33616
933	870 489	30.54505	96.59193	968	937 024	31.11270	98.38699
934	872 356	30.56141	96.64368	969	938 961	31.12876	98.43780
935	874 225	30.57777	96.69540	970	940 900	31.14482	98.48858
936	876 096	30.59412	96.74709	971	942 841	31.16087	98.53933
937	877 969	30.61046	96.79876	972	944 784	31.17691	98.59006
938	879 844	30.62679	96.85040	973	946 729	31.19295	98.64076
939	881 721	30.64311	96.90201	974	948 676	31.20897	98.69144
940	883 600	30.65942	96.95360	975	950 625	31.22499	98.74209
941	885 481	30.67572	97.00515	976	952 576	31.24100	98.79271
942	887 364	30.69202	97.05668	977	954 529	31.25700	98.84331
943	889 249	30.70831	97.10819	978	956 484	31.27299	98.89388
944	891 136	30.72458	97.15966	979	958 441	31.28898	98.94443
945	893 025	30.74085	97.21111	980	960 400	31.30495	98.99495
946	894 916	30.75711	97.26253	981	962 361	31.32092	99.04544
947	896 809	30.77337	97.31393	982	964 324	31.33688	99.09591
948	898 704	30.78961	97.36529	983	966 289	31.35283	99.14636
949	900 601	30.80584	97.41663	984	968 256	31.36877	99.19677
950	902 500	30.82207	97.46794	985	970 225	31.38471	99.24717
951	904 401	30.83829	97.51923	986	972 196	31.40064	99.29753
952	906 304	30.85450	97.57049	987	974 169	31.41656	99.34787
953	908 200	30.87070	97.62172	988	976 144	31.43247	99.39819
954	910 116	30.88689	97.67292	989	978 121	31.44837	99.44848
955	912 025	30.90307	97.72410	990	980 100	31.46427	99.49874
956	913 936	30.91925	97.77525	991	982 081	31.48015	99.54898
957	915 849	30.93542	97.82638	992	984 064	31.49603	99.59920
958	917 764	30.95158	97.87747	993	986 049	31.51190	99.64939
959	919 681	30.96773	97.92855	994	988 036	31.52777	99.69955
960	921 600	30.98387	97.97959	995	990 025	31.54362	99.74969
961	923 521	31.00000	98.03061	996	992 016	31.55947	99.79980
962	925 444	31.01612	98.08160	997	994 009	31.57531	99.84989
963	927 369	31.03224	98.13256	998	996 004	31.59114	99.89995
964	929 296	31.04835	98.18350	999	998 001	31.60966	99.94999
				1000	1000 000	31.62278	100.00000

Table 3 Random Digits

Line/Col.	(1)	(2)	(3)	(4)	(5)	(6)	(7)	(8)	(9)	(10)	(11)	(12)	(13)	(14)
1	10480	15011	01536	02011	81647	91646	69179	14194	62590	36207	20969	99570	91291	90700
2	22368	46573	25595	85393	30995	89198	27982	53402	93965	34095	52666	19174	39615	99505
3	24130	48360	22527	97265	76393	64809	15179	24830	49340	32081	30680	19655	63348	58629
4	42167	93093	06243	61680	07856	16376	39440	53537	71341	57004	00849	74917	97758	16379
5	37570	39975	81837	16656	06121	91782	60468	81305	49684	60672	14110	06927	01263	54613
6	77921	06907	11008	42751	27756	53498	18602	70659	90655	15053	21916	81825	44394	42880
7	99562	72905	56420	69994	98872	31016	71194	18738	44013	48840	63213	21069	10634	12952
8	96301	91977	05463	07972	18876	20922	94595	56869	69014	60045	18425	84903	42508	32307
9	89579	14342	63661	10281	17453	18103	57740	84378	25331	12566	58678	44947	05585	56941
10	85475	36857	53342	53988	53060	59533	38867	62300	08158	17983	16439	11458	18593	64952
11	28918	69578	88231	33276	70997	79936	56865	05859	90106	31595	01547	85590	91610	78188
12	63553	40961	48235	03427	49626	69445	18663	72695	52180	20847	12234	90511	33703	90322
13	09429	93969	52636	92737	88974	33488	36320	17617	30015	08272	84115	27156	30613	74952
14	10365	61129	87529	85689	48237	52267	67689	93394	01511	26358	85104	20285	29975	89868
15	07119	97336	71048	08178	77233	13916	47564	81056	97735	85977	29372	74461	28551	90707
16	51085	12765	51821	51259	77452	16308	60756	92144	49442	53900	70960	63990	75601	40719
17	02368	21382	52404	60268	89368	19885	55322	44819	01188	65255	64835	44919	05944	55157
18	01011	54092	33362	94904	31273	04146	18594	29852	71585	85030	51132	01915	92747	64951
19	52162	53916	46369	58586	23216	14513	83149	98736	23495	64350	94738	17752	35156	35749
20	07056	97628	33787	09998	42698	06691	76988	13602	51851	46104	88916	19509	25625	58104
21	48663	91245	85828	14346	09172	30168	90229	04734	59193	22178	30421	61666	99904	32812
22	54164	58492	22421	74103	47070	25306	76468	26384	58151	06646	21524	15227	96909	44592
23	32639	32363	05597	24200	13363	38005	94342	28728	35806	06912	17012	64161	18296	22851
24	29334	27001	87637	87308	58731	00256	45834	15398	46557	41135	10367	07684	36188	18510
25	02488	33062	28834	07351	19731	92420	60952	61280	50001	67658	32586	86679	50720	94953

Abridged from *Handbook of Tables for Probability and Statistics*, Second Edition, edited by William H. Beyer (Cleveland: The Chemical Rubber Company, 1968.) Reproduced by permission of the publishers, The Chemical Rubber Company.

Line/Col.	(1)	(2)	(3)	(4)	(5)	(6)	(7)	(8)	(9)	(10)	(11)	(12)	(13)	(14)
26	81525	72295	04839	96423	24878	82651	66566	14778	76797	14780	13300	87074	79666	95725
27	29676	20591	68086	26432	46901	20849	89768	81536	86645	12659	92259	57102	80428	25280
28	00742	57392	39064	66432	84673	40027	32832	61362	98947	96067	64760	64584	96096	98253
29	05366	04213	25669	26422	44407	44048	37937	63904	45766	66134	75470	66520	34693	90449
30	91921	26418	64117	94305	26766	25940	39972	22209	71500	64568	91402	42416	07844	69618
31	00582	04711	87917	77341	42206	35126	74087	99547	81817	42607	43808	76655	62028	76630
32	00725	69984	62797	56170	86324	88072	76222	36086	84637	93161	76038	65855	77919	88006
33	69011	65795	95876	55293	18988	27354	26575	08625	40801	59920	29841	80150	12777	48501
34	25976	57948	29888	88604	67917	48708	18912	82271	65424	69774	33611	54262	85963	03547
35	09763	83473	73577	12908	30883	18317	28290	33797	05998	41688	34952	37888	38917	88050
36	91567	42595	27958	30134	04024	86335	29880	99730	55536	84855	29080	09250	79656	73211
37	17955	56349	90999	49127	20044	59931	06115	20542	18059	02008	73708	83517	36103	42791
38	46503	18584	18845	49618	02304	51038	20655	58727	28168	15475	56942	53389	20562	87338
39	92157	89634	94824	78171	84610	82834	09922	25417	44137	48413	25555	21246	35509	20468
40	14577	62765	35605	81263	39667	47358	56873	56307	61607	49518	89656	20103	77490	18062
41	98427	07523	33362	64270	01638	92477	66969	98420	04880	45585	46565	04102	46880	45709
42	34914	63976	88720	82765	34476	17032	87589	40836	32427	70002	70663	88863	77775	69348
43	70060	28877	39475	46473	23219	53416	94970	25832	69975	94884	19661	72828	00102	66794
44	53976	54914	06990	67245	68350	82948	11398	42878	80287	88267	47363	46634	06541	97809
45	76072	29515	40980	07391	58745	25774	22987	80059	39911	96189	41151	14222	60697	59583
46	90725	52210	83974	29992	65831	38857	50490	83765	55657	14361	31720	57375	56228	41546
47	64364	67412	33339	31926	14883	24413	59744	92351	97473	89286	35931	04110	23726	51900
48	08962	00358	31662	25388	61642	34072	81249	35648	56891	69352	48373	45578	78547	81788
49	95012	68379	93526	70765	10592	04542	76463	54328	02349	17247	28865	14777	62730	92277
50	15664	10493	20492	38391	91132	21999	59516	81652	27195	48223	46751	22923	32261	85653
51	16408	81899	04153	53381	79401	21438	83035	92350	36693	31238	59649	91754	72772	02338
52	18629	81953	05520	91962	04739	13092	97662	24822	94730	06496	35090	04822	86774	98289
53	73115	35101	47498	87637	99016	71060	88824	71013	18735	20286	23153	72924	35165	43040
54	57491	16703	23167	49323	45021	33132	12544	41035	80780	45393	44812	12515	98931	91202
55	30405	83946	23792	14422	15059	45799	22716	19792	09983	74353	68668	30429	70735	25499
56	16631	35006	85900	98275	32388	52390	16815	69298	82732	38480	73817	32523	41961	44437
57	96773	20206	42559	78985	05300	22164	24369	54224	35083	19687	11052	91491	60383	19746
58	38935	64202	14349	82074	66523	44133	00697	35552	35970	19124	63318	29686	03387	59846
59	31624	76384	17403	53363	44167	64486	64758	75366	76554	31601	12614	33072	60332	92325
60	78919	19474	23632	27889	47914	02584	37680	20801	72152	39339	34806	08930	85001	87820
61	03931	33309	57047	74211	63445	17361	62825	39908	05607	91284	68833	25570	38818	46920
62	74426	33278	43972	10119	89917	15665	52872	73823	73144	88662	88970	74492	51805	99378
63	09066	00903	20795	95452	92648	45454	09552	88515	16553	51125	79375	97596	16296	66092
64	42238	12426	87025	14267	20979	04508	64535	31355	86064	29472	47689	05974	52468	16834
65	16153	08002	26504	41744	81959	65642	74240	56302	00033	67107	77510	70625	28725	34191

Table 3   239

66	21457	40742	29820	29400	21840	15035	34537	33310	06116	95240	15957	16572	06004
67	21581	57802	02050	17937	37621	47075	42080	97403	48626	68995	43805	33336	21597
68	55612	78095	83197	05810	24813	86902	60397	16489	03264	88525	42786	05269	92532
69	44657	66999	99324	84463	60563	79312	93454	68876	25471	93911	25650	12682	73572
70	91340	84979	46949	37949	61023	43997	15263	80644	43942	89203	71795	99533	50501
71	91227	21199	31935	84067	05462	35216	14486	29891	68607	41867	14951	91696	85065
72	50001	38140	66321	72163	09533	12151	06878	91903	18749	34405	56087	82790	70925
73	65390	05224	72958	81406	39147	25549	48542	42627	45233	57202	94617	23772	07896
74	27504	96131	83944	10573	08619	64482	73923	36152	05184	94142	25299	84387	34925
75	37169	94851	39117	00959	16487	65536	49071	39782	17095	02330	74301	00275	48280
76	11508	70025	51111	19444	66499	71945	05422	13442	78675	84081	66938	93654	59894
77	37449	30362	06694	04052	53115	62757	95348	78662	11163	81651	50245	34971	52924
78	46515	70331	85922	57015	15765	97161	17869	45349	61796	66345	81073	49106	79860
79	30986	81223	42416	21532	30502	32305	86482	05174	07901	54339	58861	74818	46942
80	63798	64995	46583	44160	78128	83991	42865	92520	83531	80377	35909	81250	54238
81	82486	84846	99254	43218	50076	21361	64816	51202	88124	41870	52689	51275	83556
82	21885	32906	92431	64297	51674	64126	62570	26123	05155	59194	52799	28225	85762
83	60336	98782	07408	13564	59089	26445	29789	85205	41001	12535	12133	14645	23541
84	43937	46891	24010	86355	33941	25786	54990	71899	15475	95434	98227	21824	19585
85	97656	63175	89303	07100	92063	21942	18611	47348	20203	18534	03862	78095	50136
86	03299	01221	05418	55758	92237	26759	86367	21216	98442	08303	56613	91511	75928
87	79626	06486	03574	07785	76020	79924	25651	83325	88428	85076	72811	22717	50585
88	85636	68335	47539	65651	11977	02510	26113	99447	68645	34327	15152	55230	93448
89	18039	14367	61337	12143	46609	32989	74014	64708	00533	35398	58408	13261	47908
90	08362	15656	60627	65648	16764	53412	09013	07832	41574	17639	82163	60859	75567
91	79556	29068	69882	15387	12856	66227	38358	22478	73373	88732	09443	82558	05250
92	92608	82674	63003	17075	27698	98204	63863	11951	34648	88022	56148	34925	57031
93	23982	25835	55417	12293	02753	14827	23235	35071	99704	37543	11601	35503	85171
94	09915	96306	52667	28395	14186	00821	80703	70426	75647	76310	88717	37890	40129
95	59037	33300	94964	69927	76123	50842	43834	86654	70959	79725	93872	28817	19233
96	42488	78077	05908	34136	79180	97526	43092	04098	73571	80799	76536	71255	64239
97	46764	86273	26695	31204	36692	40202	35275	57306	55543	53203	18098	47625	88684
98	03237	45430	16275	90816	17349	88298	90183	36600	78806	06216	95787	42579	90730
99	86591	81482	36478	14972	90053	89534	76036	49199	43716	97548	04379	46370	28672
100	38534	01715	62247	65680	43772	39560	12918	86537	62738	19636	51132	25739	56947

Answers

Chapter 4

4.1 $\hat{p} = 5/6$ $B = .1313$

4.2 $n = 128$

4.3 $\bar{y} = 12.5$ $B = 7.0412$

4.4 $\hat{\tau} = 125{,}000$ $B = 70412.4989$

4.5 $\hat{\mu}_1 = 2.30$ $\hat{\mu}_2 = 4.52$ $B = .0703$ $B = .0858$

4.6 $\hat{p} = .625$ $B = .1551$

4.7 $\hat{\mu} = 2.0$ $B = .9381$

4.8 $\hat{p} = .43$ $B = .0312$

4.9 $n = 2392$

4.10 $\hat{\tau} = 100$ $B = 31.29$

4.11 $\hat{\mu} = 2.1$ $B = .1697$

4.12 $n = 4$

4.13 $\hat{\mu} = 5.0125$ $B = .8711$

4.14 $\hat{p} = \dfrac{11}{60}$ $B = .0948$

4.15 $n = 87$

4.16 $\hat{\tau} = 37{,}800$ $B = 3379.94$

4.17 $n = 400$

Chapter 5

5.1 $\hat{p}_{st} = .3004$ $B = .1166$

5.2 $n_1 = 18$, $n_2 = 10$, $n_3 = 2$

5.3 $\hat{\tau} = 1903.90$ $B = 676.80$

5.4 $\bar{y}_{st} = 13208.63$ $B = 560.485$

5.5 $n = 27$, $n_1 = 16$, $n_2 = 7$, $n_3 = 4$

5.6 $\bar{y}_{st} = 59.78$ $B = 2.98$

5.7 $n_1 = 11$, $n_2 = 21$, $n_3 = 18$

5.8 $n = 33$

5.9 $n = 32$

5.10 $\hat{\tau} = 50505.60$ $B = 8663.124$

5.11 $n = 156$

5.12 $n = 29$

5.13 $n = 182$ $n_1 = 35$, $n_2 = 15$, $n_3 = 61$, $n_4 = 71$

5.14 $\hat{p}_{st} = .663$ $B = .0507$

5.15 $n = 58$ $n_1 = 11$, $n_2 = 5$, $n_3 = 19$, $n_4 = 23$

Chapter 6

6.1 $\hat{\tau}_y = 1589.5522$ $B = 186.3176$

6.2 $\hat{\tau}_y = 2958.3333$ $B = 730.13697$

6.3 $r = .2113$ $B = .0126$

6.4 $\hat{\tau}_y = 145943.7809$ $B = 7353.67$

6.5 $\hat{\mu}_y = 1186.5348$ $B = 59.79$

6.6 $\hat{\mu}_y = 17.5892$ $B = .2710$

6.7 $\hat{\mu}_y = 4.1646$ $B = .0847$

6.8 $r = .283$ $B = .0114$

6.9 $\hat{\tau}_y = 5492.3077$ $B = 428.4381$

6.10 $r = 1.037$ $B = .001391$

6.11 $\hat{\mu}_y = 1061.0376$ $B = 139.9468$

6.12 $\hat{\tau}_y = 231,611.86$ $B = 3073.83$

6.13 $n = 13$

Chapter 7

7.1 $\bar{y} = 19.73077$ $B = 1.78$

7.2 $\hat{\tau} = N\bar{y}_t = 12312$ $B = 3175.067$

7.3 $\hat{\tau} = M\bar{y} = 14008.846$ $B = 1110.7845$

7.4 $n = 14$

7.5 $\bar{y} = 51.56$ $B = 1.344$

7.6 $n = 13$

7.7 $\hat{p} = .709$ $B = .048$

7.8 $n = 7$

7.9 $\bar{y} = 40.1688$ $B = .6406$

7.10 $\hat{\tau} = 157{,}020$ $B = 6927.875$

7.11 $n = 30$

7.12 $\bar{y} = 16.005$ $B = .0215$

7.13 $\hat{p} = .57$ $B = .0307$

7.14 $n = 21$

7.15 $\bar{y} = 5.91$ $B = .3224$

7.16 $\hat{p} = .4$ $B = .1165$

Chapter 8

8.1 $\hat{p}_{sy} = .66$ $B = .0637$

8.2 $n = 1636$

8.3 $\bar{y}_{sy} = 11.9447$ $B = .0259$

8.4 $n = 28$

8.5 $\bar{y}_{sy} = 2007.1111$

8.6 $\hat{p} = .81$ $B = .0363$

8.7 $n = 1432$

8.8 $\hat{\tau} = 127{,}500$ $B = 30137.0593$

8.9 $n = 259$

8.10 $\bar{y}_{sy} = 3.54$ $B = .406$

8.11 $\bar{y}_{sy} = 225.4717$ $B = 6.7524$

8.12 $\hat{\tau} = 48{,}680$ $B = 1370.3446$

8.13 $\bar{y}_{sy} = 7038.0952$ $B = 108.7363$

8.14 $\hat{p}_{sy} = .738$ $B = .1041$

8.15 $\hat{\tau} = 4{,}400$ $B = 792.273$

Chapter 9

9.1 $\hat{\mu}_r = 9.3789$ $B = 1.4577$

9.2 $\hat{\mu} = 9.5593$ $B = 1.3707$

9.3 $\hat{p} = .2865$ $B = .15$

9.4 $\hat{p} = .351$ $B = .28$
9.5 $\hat{\tau} = 3980.7$ $B = 136.3027$
9.6 $\hat{p} = .1200$ $B = .0829$
9.7 $\hat{\tau} = 1276.2425$ $B = 552.2402$
9.8 $\hat{\mu} = 7.9333$ $B = .0924$

Chapter 10

10.4 $N = 444.444 \approx 445$ $B = 150.596$
10.5 $\tilde{N} = 1811$ $B = 344.512$
10.6 $\hat{N} = 10,868$ $B = 715.82086$
10.7 $\hat{N} = 3348.2143$ $B = 445.10$
10.8 $\hat{N} = 200$ $B = 78.88$
10.9 $\dfrac{\hat{V}(\hat{N})}{N} = 12.67$ or $t \approx 625, n \approx 625$
10.10 $\hat{N} = 1067$ $B = 507.7182$
10.11 $\hat{N} = 750$ $B = 441.588$
10.13 $\hat{N} = 250$ $B = 52.04$

Chapter 11

11.1 $\bar{y} = 407.125$ $B = 93.703$
11.2 $\bar{y} = 5.26$ $B = .7889$
11.3 $\bar{y} = 23.6113$ $B = 9.0972$
11.4 $\hat{\tau} = 1794.455$ $B = 864.2327$
11.5 $\hat{\tau}_1 = 1959.7338$ $B = 763.5104$
11.6 $\bar{y} = 9.8042$ $B = 2.3758$
11.7 $\hat{\tau} = 3866.7633$ $B = 1171.2750$
11.8 $\hat{\tau}_1 = 4117.764$ $B = 999.8094$
11.9 $\hat{p} = .875$ $B = .1052$
11.10 $\hat{p} = .125$ $B = .1377$

Index

Allocation of the sample, 64, 76
  Neyman, 67
  optimum, 64
  proportional, 70
Animal populations, 187
Average cluster size, 124

Biased estimator, 14
Bound on the error of estimation, 15

Central Limit Theorem, 13
Cluster sampling, 23, 121
  estimator of a mean, 124
  estimator of a proportion, 137
  estimator of a total, 127, 129
Coefficient of linear correlation, 11, 13
Correlation, 11, 13
Cost, 19, 64
Covariance, 11, 12

Design of the sample survey, 20

Element, 20
Empirical Rule, 6, 7, 13, 15
Error of estimation, 15, 22
Estimation, 14
  interval, 14
  point, 14
Estimator, 14
  of population mean, 33, 34, 57, 101, 124, 150, 163, 174, 179, 202, 205
  of population proportion, 43, 44, 73, 137, 157, 181
  of population ratio, 96
  of population size, 189, 191
  of population total, 33, 38, 59, 98, 127, 129, 155, 163, 177, 207, 209
Event, 8
  simple, 8
Expected value, 10
Experiment, 2, 8

Finite population correction, 35
Frame, 21

Haphazard sampling, 32

Inference, 1, 3
Interpenetrating subsamples, 202
    estimator of a mean, 202
Interval estimation, 14
Interviews
    personal, 25
    telephone, 25

Mean
    estimator of, *see* Estimator
    population, 6
    sample, 6

Neyman allocation, 67
Nonresponse, 24

Optimum allocation, 64
Ordered population, 151

Parameters, 14
Periodic population, 151, 152
Population, 1, 20
Population, types of
    ordered, 151
    periodic, 151, 152
    random, 151
Probability, 8, 9
Probability distribution, 9, 10
Proportion, 43
    estimator of, 43, 44, 74
Proportional allocation, 70

Questionnaire, 25
    dichotomous, 26
    mail, 25
    multiple-choice, 26
    open-end, 26
    self-administered, 25

Random number tables, 32
Random population, 151
Random response, 210, 211
Random sampling, 22, 31
Random variables
    continuous, 10
    discrete, 9

Ratio estimation, 23, 93
    mean, 101
    ratio, 96
    total, 98
    using simple random sampling, 95
Repeated systematic sampling, 161
    estimating a mean, 161
Representative sampling, 32

Sample, 1, 21
Sample, allocation of, 64, 76
Sample point, 8
Sample size, 40, 42, 46, 61, 76, 105,
        108, 110, 133, 136, 140, 159, 160,
        192
Sample standard deviation, 6, 7
Sample survey design, 31
Sampling unit, 20
Sample variance, 6, 7
Simple random sampling, 22, 31
    estimator of a mean, 34
    estimator of a proportion, 44
    estimator of a total, 38
Standard deviation, 6, 7
Stratified random sampling, 23, 53, 54
    estimator of a mean, 57
    estimator of a proportion, 74
    estimator of a total, 59
Stratum, 53
Subpopulation, 204
    estimator of a mean, 205
    estimator of a total, 207, 209
Subsidiary variable, 93
Survey, 2
Systematic sampling, 23, 147
    estimator of a mean, 150, 163
    estimator of a proportion, 157
    estimator of a total, 155, 163

Tchebysheff's Theorem, 6, 7, 15
Total, estimator of, *see* Estimator
Two-stage cluster sampling, 171
    estimator of a mean, 174, 179
    estimator of a proportion, 181
    estimator of a total, 177

Unbiased estimator, 14

Variance
    population, 6, 7, 11
    sample, 6, 7

Wildlife population, 187
    estimator of population size, 189,
       191